GW00658654

ONE GOOD THING

A full-length drama by
Don Zolidis

www.youthplays.com
info@youthplays.com
424-703-5315

One Good Thing © 2006 Don Zolidis
All rights reserved. ISBN 978-1-62088-019-7.

Caution: This play is fully protected under the copyright laws of the United States of America, Canada, the British Commonwealth and all other countries of the copyright union and is subject to royalty for all performances including but not limited to professional, amateur, charity and classroom whether admission is charged or presented free of charge.

Reservation of Rights: This play is the property of the author and all rights for its use are strictly reserved and must be licensed by his representative, YouthPLAYS. This prohibition of unauthorized professional and amateur stage presentations extends also to motion pictures, recitation, lecturing, public reading, radio broadcasting, television, video and the rights of adaptation or translation into non-English languages.

Performance Licensing and Royalty Payments: Amateur and stock performance rights are administered exclusively by YouthPLAYS. No amateur, stock or educational theatre groups or individuals may perform this play without securing authorization and royalty arrangements in advance from YouthPLAYS. Required royalty fees for performing this play are available online at www.YouthPLAYS.com. Royalty fees are subject to change without notice. Required royalties must be paid each time this play is performed and may not be transferred to any other performance entity. All licensing requests and inquiries should be addressed to YouthPLAYS.

Author Credit: All groups or individuals receiving permission to produce this play must give the author(s) credit in any and all advertisement and publicity relating to the production of this play. The author's billing must appear directly below the title on a separate line with no other accompanying written matter. The name of the author(s) must be at least 50% as large as the title of the play. No person or entity may receive larger or more prominent credit than that which is given to the author(s) and the name of the author(s) may not be abbreviated or otherwise altered from the form in which it appears in this Play.

Publisher Attribution: All programs, advertisements, flyers or other printed material must include the following notice:
Produced by special arrangement with YouthPLAYS (www.youthplays.com).

Prohibition of Unauthorized Copying: Any unauthorized copying of this book or excerpts from this book, whether by photocopying, scanning, video recording or any other means, is strictly prohibited by law. This book may only be copied by licensed productions with the purchase of a photocopy license, or with explicit permission from YouthPLAYS.

Trade Marks, Public Figures & Musical Works: This play may contain references to brand names or public figures. All references are intended only as parody or other legal means of expression. This play may also contain suggestions for the performance of a musical work (either in part or in whole). YouthPLAYS has not obtained performing rights of these works unless explicitly noted. The direction of such works is only a playwright's suggestion, and the play producer should obtain such permissions on their own. The website for the U.S. copyright office is *http://www.copyright.gov*.

COPYRIGHT RULES TO REMEMBER

1. To produce this play, you must receive prior written permission from YouthPLAYS and pay the required royalty.

2. You must pay a royalty each time the play is performed in the presence of audience members outside of the cast and crew. Royalties are due whether or not admission is charged, whether or not the play is presented for profit, for charity or for educational purposes, or whether or not anyone associated with the production is being paid.

3. No changes, including cuts or additions, are permitted to the script without written prior permission from YouthPLAYS.

4. Do not copy this book or any part of it without written permission from YouthPLAYS.

5. Credit to the author and YouthPLAYS are required on all programs and other promotional items associated with this play's performance.

When you pay royalties, you are recognizing the hard work that went into creating the play and making a statement that a play is something of value. We think this is important, and we hope that everyone will do the right thing, thus allowing playwrights to generate income and continue to create wonderful new works for the stage.

Plays are owned by the playwrights who wrote them. Violating a playwright's copyright is a very serious matter and violates both United States and international copyright law. Infringement is punishable by actual damages and attorneys' fees, statutory damages of up to $150,000 per incident, and even possible criminal sanctions. **Infringement is theft. Don't do it.**

Have a question about copyright? Please contact us by email at info@youthplays.com or by phone at 424-703-5315. When in doubt, please ask.

CAST OF CHARACTERS

The Families:

ERYNNE O'NEILL, 17, a troubled punk girl.

ERYNNE'S FATHER, (Brad), 40ish, a former pitcher, partly disabled and unemployed.

ERYNNE'S MOTHER, (Gail), 40ish, soft-spoken and defeated.

DIERDRE O'NEILL, 14, Erynne's older sister, dead for five years.

TRAVIS ARNESON, 17, sweet, awkward, a little bit bored.

NICK ARNESON, 20, Travis' older brother, a marine.

TRAVIS' FATHER, (Jim), 45, married 23 years, going through a mid-life crisis.

TRAVIS' MOTHER, (Terri), 42, married 23 years, not going through a mid-life crisis.

Erynne's world:

NEMO, 18, her boyfriend. Charming, ruthless, a little dangerous.

TRANK, 18, a criminal from a Christian Academy.

CHUBB, 16, a thin punk girl.

SCOOTER, 17, a very strange boy.

ROHAN, 21, Scooter's older brother, a warlock.

ESMERELDA, 23, Scooter's older sister, normal in comparison.

Travis' world:

KIMBERLY WALUSCHKA, 17, his next-door neighbor, blond and beautiful.

JESSIE WALUSCHKA, 13, Kimberly's younger sister, a little weird

LILY, 13, Jessie's depressed friend.

MORGAN, 13, Jessie's friend.

KALLIE, 14, Jessie's aggressive friend.

DANICA, 13, Jessie's friend.

KATIE, 17, Kimberly's friend. A prep.

Other Characters:

MISS WINDHORST, 40ish, a flustered history teacher.

ANNOUNCING VOICE

MINISTER

NURSE

PERSONS 1-4, people at a party.

MARINES

OTHER STUDENTS

A note on the language: Some productions may wish to substitute the words in <brackets> for the words in the script to make the play more suitable for school audiences. Other language deemed unsuitable may be changed as necessary.

One Good Thing is intended for ages 13 and up, and may not be appropriate for younger audience members.

One Good Thing was originally produced at Haltom High School from October 21-24, 2005. The original cast was as follows:

ERYNNE O'NEILL	Sarah Harbison
ERYNNE'S FATHER	Chase Robinson
ERYNNE'S MOTHER	Sarah Dickerson
DIERDRE O'NEILL	Jenna McDade
TRAVIS ARNESON	Trevin McLaughlin
NICK ARNESON	Sterling Mathis
TRAVIS' FATHER	Jef Erwin
TRAVIS' MOTHER	Maeghan Gibson
NEMO	Anthony Hernandez
TRANK	Jeffrey Branch
CHUBB	Alyssa Jones
SCOOTER	Jordan Starks
ROHAN	Kevin Whiteside
ESMERELDA	Roxanne Moore
KIMBERLY WALUSCHKA	Sonia Rehman
JESSIE WALUSCHKA	Jewel Gobea
LILY	Yanina Gonzalez
MORGAN	Alysia Martinez
KALLIE	Bre Gibson
DANICA	Natalie Bodak
KATIE	Chloe Gobea
MISS WINDHORST	Christina Thompson
MINISTER	Jake Hill
NURSE	Alysia Martinez

PARTY PEOPLE

Samone Scott
David Sylvester
Chelsea Spaulding
Lauren Rowland
Kelsey Harris

MARINES

Bill Tyler
Drew Cagle
Nic Neufeld
Christian Velasco

ACT I

(Rosedale. A small town on the verge of fading entirely out of view. On stage are the shadows of buildings and trees, looming, broken, sinister. Wreckage strewn about. The scenes of the play take place scattered around the stage, carved out in pools of light. Various doorways, recessed into the edges of the city provide entrances and exits. At rise, the forestage is bare except a twin bed. ERYNNE, 17, lies on the bed stage left, writing in a journal. She wears dark, ragged clothing, many sizes too large. She wears heavy makeup and is drawn out to look as frightening as possible. Stage right, TRAVIS, 17, a skinny, unpretentious kid, holds a basketball and dribbles clumsily.)

ERYNNE: *(To the audience:)* I live in a one-story ranch house in Rosedale—our neighborhood, when I was real small, used to be pretty good, but that was before people stopped mowing their lawns and started parking their cars on their yards. And that was before the creepy sex offender moved in two doors down who keeps his door open all day long—So he can keep an eye on the neighborhood and make things safe for his own brand of insanity. Anyway, we used to have a downtown, with a movie theatre and everything, and you could even get something to eat there, but eventually all the stores closed except for the Big Lots, which kind of gobbled up the other stores around it like some kind of cancerous octopus-and you know, I love the three-liter bottles of generic soda as much as the next guy, but do we really need the gigantic rolls of toilet paper? So the Big Lots sits there like the Tower of Sauron, this malevolent, oozing pimple on the face of the town, and I guess the rot just radiated from there, and so what we have left— what we have left...what we have left is a Wal-Mart, a Target, a whole selection of fast food restaurants, and a high school. If it were me, I'd just burn the whole place down and start over.

ERYNNE'S FATHER: *(Offstage:)* Who are you talking to in there?!

ERYNNE: *(Shouting off:)* I'm on the phone!

ERYNNE'S FATHER: *(Offstage:)* Get off the phone!

ERYNNE: Get off the couch!

(Travis speaks to the audience, dribbling the basketball. He makes to take a shot.)

TRAVIS: I like it here. I mean some people have their problems with Rosedale, but really it's all right. I mean I guess it's the same as everywhere else. There isn't all that much to do. But um...anyway, it's home, you know? And that makes it cool. Not so much cool as safe. I was on the basketball team in eighth grade, which is where I learned to dribble. I played a grand total of fourteen minutes in our season. I took twenty-three shots in those fourteen minutes. I made two. Every time I touched the ball I would just...hurl it towards the basket, you know? And then I would run into people trying to get the rebound. I fouled out of three games. When we had our end of the year banquet, I got the award for most improved. But I hadn't really gotten any better, you know? I pretty much sucked in the beginning, I sucked in the middle, and I sucked hard-core at the end. So the coach gave me an award because I didn't end up quitting like they all wanted me to. My point in this is that I'm not really good at anything. My brother, on the other hand—

(NICK, 20, comes out from behind and steals the ball from Travis. He dribbles around him. Nick is wearing desert fatigues.)

NICK: Oh!

(He acts like he's going to give him the ball back, then tosses it backwards Offstage. Pause. He stares at Travis.)

You look like a retard.

TRAVIS: Shut up.

NICK: How do you stand to go outside like that?

TRAVIS: I manage.

NICK: Stand up straight.

TRAVIS: No.

NICK: Stand up straight. Do it. Do it or I'm gonna punch you in the face.

TRAVIS: Do it then.

(Nick goes to punch him. Travis flinches.)

NICK: Two for flinching.

(Nick hits Travis hard in the shoulder twice.)

TRAVIS: Ow.

NICK: Wuss.

TRAVIS: Shut up.

NICK: When are you gonna grow up?

TRAVIS: When are you gonna grow up?

NICK: I am grown up. Check this out. *(He flexes:)* Feel it. Go ahead feel it.

TRAVIS: I don't want to.

NICK: You're scared. Feel it. You know what this is? This is a muscle. Rock hard. This is what three months at Camp Pendleton does to you.

TRAVIS: I thought it made you an asshole <jerk>.

(Nick goes to punch him again. Travis doesn't flinch.)

NICK: Oh! I was an asshole <jerk> before I went. They just helped me bring it out. You gonna sign up after you graduate?

TRAVIS: No.

NICK: Why not?

TRAVIS: Cause—

NICK: Cause you're a wuss.

TRAVIS: No.

NICK: Cause you're a wuss.

TRAVIS: Cause I'm going to college.

NICK: Marines'll help you pay for college. You're not a marine though. You'll never be a marine—you'll probably be like...expert toilet cleaner or something, you know? When there's a clog on the battlefield they'll call you in.

TRAVIS: You scared?

NICK: No. Quit asking me that.

TRAVIS: I'd be scared.

NICK: That's why Uncle Sam pays me to defend the country and he pays you nothing. Because he wouldn't take you— because you're a wuss.

(Lights switch back to Erynne. She has moved to the living room. ERYNNE'S FATHER sits on the couch, watching television, beer in hand.)

ERYNNE: *(To the audience:)* My dad...well, what to say about him?

ERYNNE'S FATHER: *(At the television:)* Ah come on!

(He throws his empty beer can at the TV.)

ERYNNE: That's pretty much his main characteristic. When he saw something he didn't like, he threw something at it. Every once in a while he'd get really upset at something and he wouldn't be able to find something appropriate to throw, so he'd just kind of squirm around in the couch reaching for anything, like freaked out that something hadn't hit the television yet—if he could have thrown his own head at the TV, he would've. Actually, the screen of our TV used to be the only nice thing in the house, when he bought it, on credit, it was more expensive than his truck. But now it has all these dents and scratches in it—

ERYNNE'S FATHER: *(At the television:)* What was that!?

(He looks for something, gets up a little, and tosses a pile of mail at it.)

ERYNNE: Yeah, he's a winner. He used to work as a contractor, but then something fell on him and his left arm is down to like forty percent motion or something like that—so he gets these disability checks and that's pretty much all he does. A whole lotta nothing. So my Dad's effectively like sixty percent of a human being—apparently he was like a pitcher when he was in high school—

(He throws something else at the television.)

Which I guess explains the throwing stuff.

ERYNNE'S FATHER: *(To Erynne:)* When did you get home?

ERYNNE: I've been home.

ERYNNE'S FATHER: What did you do in school today?

ERYNNE: Nothing.

(Pause. He goes back to watching the television.)

Nice talking to you, Dad.

(She starts to leave.)

ERYNNE'S FATHER: When are you gonna get some decent clothes?

ERYNNE: Give me money to go to the mall.

ERYNNE'S FATHER: Yeah, so you can go buy jeans that are already all ripped up.

ERYNNE: I don't wear ripped jeans.

ERYNNE'S FATHER: Or your crazy black parachute pants.

ERYNNE: They're not parachute pants.

ERYNNE'S FATHER: Plumber pants. Whatever. You look suicidal.

ERYNNE: Talk to you later, Dad.

(She leaves. Lights switch to Travis and Nick.)

NICK: You got a girl?

TRAVIS: No.

NICK: Why not?

TRAVIS: I haven't met the right one yet.

(Nick laughs.)

NICK: Yeah, whatever. 'I haven't met the right one yet.' Are you like quoting some stupid movie or something? Oh I'm waiting for true love. Have you ever had a girlfriend?

TRAVIS: Yes.

NICK: Liar.

TRAVIS: I'm not.

NICK: What was her name?

TRAVIS: Jessica.

NICK: You just made that up.

TRAVIS: No I didn't.

NICK: What was her last name?

TRAVIS: Walker.

NICK: What's her phone number?

(Nick takes out his cell phone.)

What's her phone number?

TRAVIS: She doesn't have a phone.

NICK: Is she like homeless or something? Did you go out with a homeless girl? Man, that's sad, was she liked passed out the whole time? Gimme the number.

TRAVIS: No.

NICK: You're such a liar. Look—let me give you some advice—you find a girl, it doesn't matter which one, any one, and buy some dinner or whatever—like Olive Garden, take `em someplace nice—

TRAVIS: Is that what you had to do?

NICK: No but I'm better looking than you. Girls bought me dinner.

TRAVIS: They did not.

NICK: Ashley...I don't even remember her last name—remember Ashley?

TRAVIS: The chick with all the acne?

NICK: It cleared up. She bought me dinner.

TRAVIS: She was just grateful cause she had such bad skin.

NICK: No. No—she was hot. All right forget Ashley—Tara, remember her? Tara was hot—and she bought me dinner—and then we made sweet, sweet—

TRAVIS: Great.

NICK: You know why? Check this out. *(He flexes again:)* Oh! Look at it. It's beautiful. You gotta go to the gym or something. What do you weigh? One thirty?

TRAVIS: No.

NICK: What do you bench?

TRAVIS: I don't know. One fifty.

NICK: Yeah right. Let me go get my weights—I wanna see this. I'm gonna put one fifty on the rack and I'm gonna watch you try it and we'll see what happens.

TRAVIS: All right, maybe less than that.

NICK: Maybe less. Maybe. Huh. Man you are such a wuss. I'm so ashamed that I'm related to you. You're like this ghost that warns me of what I could've been if I sucked a lot more.

TRAVIS: Shut up.

NICK: You embarrass me, man. What are you gonna do when I'm gone?

TRAVIS: Sleep better.

NICK: You sleep like twenty hours a day as it is.

TRAVIS: No I don't.

NICK: What do you got to be tired from, it's not like you actually do anything. Sit around—come home from school—play video games—eat—pee—play more video games—you don't have any friends, you don't have a girl, you're sad, man. You're pathetic. I'm glad I'm not you. You know what—when

I come back—when I get home—you better not be this worthless piece of crap that I see right now—you know what I'm saying? Get out there. Talk to people. Go to the gym or something. I mean, if you're the future of America, it's pretty sad, you know? You are pretty sad.

TRAVIS: Sorry, I guess my life goal to please you hasn't been achieved.

NICK: That's right, make jokes. What do you think about that, huh? What do you think about the fact that you suck? *(He waits for a response:)* You haven't been thinking about that? Man, if I were you, that's all I'd think about.

TRAVIS: Have fun in Iraq.

NICK: I will. And when I get home—

TRAVIS: Yeah I know.

NICK: I'm serious, Travis.

TRAVIS: I hear Baghdad is nice this time of year.

NICK: It's gonna be nice when I'm through with it. Let me tell you something about the American army, all right, wimp? You know what these guys do to try and kill us? They can't actually show up, right? They can't actually say hey let's actually duke it out like men. No these guys are vermin. They put tiny little bombs on the side of the road, aimed to blow up underneath a hummer, where it's weak. And they put all kinds of stuff in there, nails, glass, anything, so that it will send as much crap flying as possible. And then they run away and they blend back in with the rest of the people: You know what that makes them? Wusses. Makes me wanna puke. Doesn't matter though, cause we're gonna exterminate 'em. Make the world safe for Starbucks.

(Pause.)

TRAVIS: Hey um...don't get blown up.

NICK: I'm not gonna get blown up, man, they're gonna get blown up.

TRAVIS: Right.

NICK: Yeah, well, keep an eye on things around here, and stop being such a wuss. It's not good for ya. And it wouldn't hurt to get yourself a girl. That's an order, mister.

TRAVIS: Uh huh.

NICK: Bye.

TRAVIS: Bye.

> *(Nick leaves. Lights switch to Erynne's bedroom. She's sitting on her bed listening to her headphones. There's a knock on the door. She doesn't hear it. Another knock. She still doesn't hear. There is a pounding on the door as someone tries to open it; it's locked.)*

ERYNNE'S FATHER: *(Shouting:)* Open the door! *(He pounds on it:)* Open the damn door or I'm gonna kick it in! Erynne! Erynne!

> *(She finally hears him.)*

ERYNNE: What!

ERYNNE'S FATHER: Open the door!

ERYNNE: You don't have to shout!

> *(She opens the door and her Father bursts in.)*

ERYNNE'S FATHER: Since when do you need a lock on your door?

ERYNNE: Since you've been trying to get in.

> *(He examines the lock, takes out a screwdriver.)*

Hey.

ERYNNE'S FATHER: What. You put this on here yourself?

ERYNNE: Chubb did it.

ERYNNE'S FATHER: Who the heck is Chubb?

ERYNNE: Chubb. You've met Chubb.

ERYNNE'S FATHER: Does he have an actual name?

ERYNNE: She's a girl.

ERYNNE'S FATHER: Does she have a name?

ERYNNE: Amy.

ERYNNE'S FATHER: Is she fat?

ERYNNE: No.

ERYNNE'S FATHER: Why's she called Chubb then?

ERYNNE: I don't know. It's a nickname.

ERYNNE'S FATHER: It's a drug name. Well you tell Chubb from me that if she comes over here and puts any more locks on your door I'm gonna slap her stupid. You got it? You don't need a lock. I don't know what you think you're gonna do in this cave of a room—

ERYNNE: Dad—

(He can't get the lock off.)

ERYNNE'S FATHER: Damn it. Look at this place. What have you got in here?

ERYNNE: Nothing.

(He begins searching the room.)

Dad what are you doing?

ERYNNE'S FATHER: Painting the walls black; colored lights everywhere. You know why people have colored lights on their walls? Cause they're on drugs.

ERYNNE: I'm not on drugs, Dad.

ERYNNE'S FATHER: Look at me. Look at me. You think I don't know what you do? I know what's going on here. I know what you're doing. And don't think you're gonna get away with it. *(He kicks at the desk:)* I said look at me.

ERYNNE: What?

ERYNNE'S FATHER: You wanna be a druggie, is that what you want?

ERYNNE: Leave me alone.

ERYNNE'S FATHER: Huh? Sit down.

ERYNNE: Go away.

ERYNNE'S FATHER: Sit down.

ERYNNE: No.

ERYNNE'S FATHER: What?

ERYNNE: Leave me alone.

ERYNNE'S FATHER: Sit your butt down.

(She stands there. He grabs her by the shoulders and throws her into a chair, standing over her.)

I'm gonna tell it to you straight. When you graduate, when you leave here, you are free to screw up your life—

ERYNNE: Dad—

ERYNNE'S FATHER: Listen to me. You are free to be a crack-addicted prostitute if you want—you are free to live on the streets and sell your body to get drugs if that's what floats your boat—but you're not doing it under my roof. And just cause I can't find anything right now doesn't mean it's not here—you understand?   You understand where you're headed?   And I'm gonna wash my hands of you.   And then you're gonna come crawling back here one day, strung out, needing money, needing a place to sleep, and you know what I'm gonna do? I'm gonna laugh at you. I'm gonna shut the door in your face, because that's what you do to me every day. Look at me. Tell me where they are and I'll go easy on you.

(She doesn't say anything.)

ERYNNE'S MOTHER: *(Offstage:)* Erynne!

ERYNNE'S FATHER: She's busy!

ERYNNE'S MOTHER: *(Offstage:)* Your friends are here!

ERYNNE'S FATHER: Tell them to go away!

ERYNNE: Tell them to come up!

(No response from below. He gets off of leaning on the chair.)

ERYNNE'S FATHER: So what are you gonna do with your friends?

ERYNNE: Hang out.

ERYNNE'S FATHER: You're grounded.   You're not going anywhere.

ERYNNE: Since when?

ERYNNE'S FATHER: Since right now.

ERYNNE: For what?

ERYNNE'S FATHER: For the lock on the door.

ERYNNE: I'm not grounded.

ERYNNE'S FATHER: Yes you are.

ERYNNE: You're not gonna stop me.

ERYNNE'S FATHER: You try anything and—

(SCOOTER, 17, CHUBB, 16, and TRANK, 18, enter. They come in a jovial mood. All three look like typical goth children, with the exception of Scooter, who is so weird that he seems strange even in comparison to the others.)

CHUBB: What's up?!

(They stop when they see her Father.)

TRANK: Hey Mr. O'Neill.

ERYNNE'S FATHER: Why can't you dress like normal people?

TRANK: *(Overlapping:)* Because we don't want to.

CHUBB: *(Overlapping:)* This is normal.

SCOOTER: *(Overlapping:)* Normal people scare me.

ERYNNE'S FATHER: You know one of these days you're gonna have to get a job. And it's all fun and good that you can walk around wearing—what is that, a dog collar? Are you a dog?

CHUBB: Bark bark.

ERYNNE'S FATHER: What is wrong with you? Huh? You see what happens when you walk into an office wearing that.

TRANK: I have a job.

ERYNNE'S FATHER: Where do you work?

TRANK: At a Christian Youth Ministry.

(Pause. Erynne's Father doesn't know what to say.)

ERYNNE'S FATHER: Are you supposed to be Chubb?

CHUBB: Um...I think so.

ERYNNE'S FATHER: Why are you called Chubb?

CHUBB: Cause I'm so fat.

(He looks at her quizzically.)

CHUBB: It's ironic. I'm filled with irony. Do you know what irony is?

ERYNNE'S FATHER: Erynne's grounded. She's not going anywhere. And I want you people out of my house in thirty minutes or I'm calling the cops.

(He leaves.)

CHUBB: *(Calling out after him:)* Hey one of these days you're gonna have to stop being a total—<asshole>

(He comes back fast.)

ERYNNE'S FATHER: What was that? You wanna tell that to my face?

CHUBB: No.

ERYNNE'S FATHER: I didn't think so.

(He waits there, looking at them. Then he leaves. They shut the door.)

CHUBB: Picking on a sixteen year-old girl. Yeah, you're tough.

ERYNNE: I'm sorry guys.

CHUBB: Not your fault.

TRANK: Is it me or does your Dad become more of a jerk every day?

ERYNNE: I don't think it's you.

SCOOTER: He scares me.

TRANK: Yeah, whatever.

SCOOTER: He's like a demon.

ERYNNE: He's not a demon, he's my Dad.

SCOOTER: You don't know that. He could be a demon. He could be possessed. Perhaps we should perform an exorcism on him.

ERYNNE: Is there a reason you guys brought Scooter over? Cause he's freaking me out.

CHUBB: We're looking after him. He just kinda found us.

ERYNNE: Okay. Where's Nemo?

CHUBB: I don't know, he's your boyfriend.

TRANK: We were gonna go look for him. His cell phone's off.

ERYNNE: He probably lost it again.

CHUBB: Probably.

ERYNNE: I'm grounded, though.

TRANK: Who cares?

ERYNNE: No I really can't go.

TRANK: What's he gonna do, call the police?

SCOOTER: He might have magical powers. He could put a curse on you.

ERYNNE: Right.

TRANK: We just go out the window. *(He opens the window:)* Come on. Chubb, lock the door.

ERYNNE: Guys.

CHUBB: Don't you wanna see Nemo?

ERYNNE: Yeah.

TRANK: Come on. What else are you gonna do? Sit here and get yelled at by your Dad?

ERYNNE: All right.

(Chubb, Trank, and Erynne go out the window. Scooter remains in the room. He gets under the covers in the bed and goes to sleep. Lights switch back to Travis, in school. Several students sit in the class, including KIMBERLY, 17, blonde and beautiful. He sits directly behind her. MISS WINDHORST, 45, is at the imaginary blackboard. The Announcements are on.)

MISS WINDHORST: All right quiet!

ANNOUNCER: *(Voice:)* Good morning Rosedale High School. These are your morning announcements. Please pause for a moment of silence.

MISS WINDHORST: Quiet!

(Erynne enters, hurrying.)

That's your third tardy Erynne.

ERYNNE: Oh come on. I had to talk to the counselor.

MISS WINDHORST: Couldn't you do that after school?

ERYNNE: I'm having severe mental problems.

ANNOUNCER: All right, let's remember all the people out there fighting for our freedom. They sure are doing a good job. First up: The Math Club is meeting today after school in room 212. Today's discussion topic: The Quadratic Formula. So you better read that before you show up or you won't be allowed into the room. Today's meeting for guys who want to beat up math nerds is in room 212 after school. *(Short pause.)* I'm just kidding about that guys.

MISS WINDHORST: All right guys, open your books to page—

ANNOUNCER: This is from the wrestling team: There are still openings in the squad, so guys, if you want roll around and get sweaty with another guy wearing a leotard...no wait, that's not what it says here. If you want to join a team of exciting physical competition, stop by the auxiliary gym today after school.

(Pause.)

MISS WINDHORST: We were talking about George Washington's retreat from New York—

ANNOUNCER: And it's about time to get tickets for the Homecoming Dance. So, guys out there, if you're totally obsessed with the blonde girl sitting in front of you and you wish to God that she knew who you were, now's about the time to ask her to the dance and get shot down and be miserable for the rest of the year because you're a hopeless loser. But remember, even if she shoots you down the first time, you still have the opportunity to be idiotically in love with her for the rest of the year and get shot down a few more times because you have this stupid hope that she's going to change her mind. She's not going to change her mind, guys, she doesn't like you.

(Pause. Travis looks up.)

MISS WINDHORST: This was quite a defeat for—

ANNOUNCER: And that's all we have for today. Remember: Be healthy, happy, and full of pep. Go Wildcats.

(He makes a growling sound.)

MISS WINDHORST: He had lost quite a few of his men in the battle, so he was left, really, with a skeleton crew.

ANNOUNCER: One more thing, the girls' soccer coach is still looking for a manager. So if you want to be around a bunch of... Anyway, they're looking for a manager.

(NEMO, 18, a ragged-looking yet charming punk kid, darts into the classroom and crouches next to Erynne. He is passing a note to her.)

MISS WINDHORST: Excuse me?

NEMO: It's really important. *(To Erynne:)* So what are you up to tonight?

ERYNNE: Not much.

NEMO: You should come on over.

ERYNNE: Okay.

MISS WINDHORST: What is your name?

NEMO: Names are just labels we give to things we don't understand. *(Back to Erynne:)* I'll see you around eight, all right?

ERYNNE: Cool.

MISS WINDHORST: I'm trying to teach a class here.

NEMO: You can go ahead and teach the class, I'll be quiet.

MISS WINDHORST: Leave, please.

NEMO: You're looking very nice today. *(To Erynne:)* What's her name?

ERYNNE: Miss Windhorst.

NEMO: Miss Windhorst.

MISS WINDHORST: Leave.

NEMO: Do you think I'm a bad kid?

MISS WINDHORST: I don't care.

NEMO: You don't have to be rude about it.

MISS WINDHORST: Erynne, is this your friend?

NEMO: I don't know that girl at all. She's just some skank that's trying to seduce me.

(Miss Windhorst is trying to escort Nemo out.)

Whoah, whoah, come on. What if I just wanted to sit in on the class? Acquire some learning? You're interfering in my education.

MISS WINDHORST: Do you even attend this school?

NEMO: Occasionally.

(She tries to push at him.)

Hey. Hey. Ow.

(She pushes him.)

That's assault. You guys all saw that. You just assaulted me, I'm going to sue. What if I fell into something sharp... *(He tries to fall into something sharp:)* And ruined my face, you know? I could be scarred for life. I would never work again. I'd be injured—it would all be your fault.

MISS WINDHORST: Get out.

NEMO: Geez, why didn't you just say so? You don't have to be such an old b— *(He stops, then smiles:)* You know I was going to call you a bitch <biyatch> but then I stopped myself.

(He leaves. Miss Windhorst takes a moment to de-tense.)

MISS WINDHORST: Okay, where were we? Washington's army—

(The Bell rings. The kids get up instantly. Travis tries to stay near Kimberly.)

TRAVIS: Hey Kimberly.

KIMBERLY: Hi.

(Pause. She's leaving.)

TRAVIS: How's it going?

KIMBERLY: All right.

(Pause. She leaves. Travis speaks to the audience.)

TRAVIS: Kimberly Lee Waluschka. To say that I was madly in love with her from a distance is something of an understatement because I lived next door — well, actually, she moved in about three months after we did — I already knew her, and I already had a crush on her, but when I found out she was moving in next to us, something snapped in my tiny little mind. I mean, it was like, suddenly I was obsessed. Suddenly I was making anagrams out of her name and counting the syllables to try to figure out if we destined for each other. I managed to sit behind her in American History, which pretty much consisted of me staring directly into her back and fantasizing about diving into a swimming pool filled with her hair. Homecoming. The dance. The important dance, and I knew she wasn't going out with anyone and here was my chance. I volunteered to mow their lawn, and I'd make sure to do it without my shirt on, and I'd do a whole bunch of push-ups before I went out there to make sure I was bulked up and everything, so when I mowed she'd see me and be so moved by my sunburned, scrawny physique that she would fall in love with me. Needless to say, that hadn't worked just yet. Sometimes I'd even go out there and throw a Frisbee to myself, you know toss it up in the air real high so she could see how athletic I was? That was...that hadn't quite succeeded yet either. So of course I figured that the best way to ask her to the dance, even though I lived next door, was to call her on the phone.

(Travis moves back into his home. He picks up the phone. We hear it ringing three times. Travis paces, takes deep breaths, and stretches his mouth while he waits for it to pick up.)

JESSIE'S VOICE: You've reached the Waluschkas. No one is available to take your call right now — what? What? Shut up I'm trying to do the answering machine message! Well I don't know — go look in your room — I hate you!

(The tone sounds. He hangs up, then hits himself in the head with the phone. He calls again, breathing once more. The machine picks up.)

You've reached the Waluschkas. No one is available to take your call right now — what? What? Shut up I'm trying to do the answering machine message! Well I don't know — go look in your room — I hate you!

(The tone sounds again.)

TRAVIS: Um...hi...uh...Kimberly, it's Travis, and I was wondering if you got the History homework today, so...uh...give me a call. *(He sets the phone down:)* That was Wednesday.

(Lights switch to the classroom. He sits behind Kimberly in class, staring at her. The bell rings.)

So um...hey.

KIMBERLY: Hey.

(Pause. Travis tries to think of something to say.)

TRAVIS: Did you get that message last night?

KIMBERLY: Yeah.

TRAVIS: Oh. *(Pause. Travis is back to the audience:)* Thursday night.

(He calls up.)

JESSIE'S VOICE: You've reached the Waluschkas. No one is available to take your call right now—what? What? Shut up I'm trying to do the answering machine message! Well I don't know—go look in your room—I hate you!

(It rings.)

TRAVIS: This is a message for Kimberly. This is Travis...um...from next door. I was wondering if you were...doing anything right now cause I was thinking that maybe you could help me with history...so...uh...give me a call. *(Back to the audience:)* So that was Thursday. And then there was Friday.

(Travis hangs up and stares at the phone. It rings. He goes to pick it up, then stops, letting it ring twice. He picks it up.)

Hello?

(Click.)

A star sixty-nine revealed that it had come from Kimberly's house.

(He dials again.)

JESSIE'S VOICE: You've reached the Waluschkas. No one is available to take your call right now—what? What? Shut up I'm trying to do the answering machine message! Well I don't know—go look in your room—I hate you!

(The machine rings.)

TRAVIS: Oh. Uh—just wondering if you called. So—uh—it's Travis. Next door. Bye.

(He hangs up. Stares at the phone.)

✳ So that was Friday. Which also happened to be the night my Dad decided to leave us.

(Lights switch to Erynne, in the wreckage of some place. Nemo sits nearby.)

ERYNNE: When I was twelve, my older sister Dierdre was killed in a car accident. It wasn't exactly an accident. Her and her friends were car surfing, which is where one kid gets on top of the car and either stands up or just holds on as they drive around like crazy. And so they were doing this in the park, and I guess some of her friends had gone already—and I never really knew if she was drunk or not while she was doing this, but I guess she probably was, anyway, they went around a corner and she rolled off and hit her head on the pavement really hard—cracked open her skull, left part of her brain on the road—the doctors thought they'd be able to save her life for a while, just that she'd have some permanent brain damage from the...you know, from the leaving part of her brain on the pavement—I guess you expect to not be all that all right when they're picking little pebbles out of your skull—but the surgeon who was in charge of putting her brain back together screwed up and she died on the operating table. My Mom sued. The case was dismissed. We ended up with nothing. So, anyway, now I'm an only child—so...so there it is. *(She turns to Nemo:)* So there's life and there's death, you know? There's a legend...about a woman named Dierdre...well I mean, like we're Irish and everything, and Dierdre was supposedly the most beautiful woman on the whole island—

NEMO: *(To Erynne:)* She probably smelled all Irish fresh and everything.

ERYNNE: *(To Nemo:)* But anyway, she was so beautiful that people kept on fighting over her and killing each other in order to kidnap her. So finally this guy kills her true love and takes her away to be with him. But instead of being his wife, Dierdre kills herself by smashing her head on a rock repeatedly. I think about that. About having the guts to be able to do that. I mean, to not just hit yourself once, but to do it again and again...and maybe that's what happened to my sister...maybe she had just had enough—of this place, of the ruin, of this slow crumble.

NEMO: You want a beer?

ERYNNE: No.

NEMO: What's wrong?

ERYNNE: My parents are freaking out on me.

NEMO: Join the club.

ERYNNE: They're talking about boarding up my windows. Or putting me in rehab.

NEMO: That sucks. They're not gonna put you in rehab, though, that costs money. Your parents are too cheap.

ERYNNE: Yeah, no kidding.

NEMO: You know what would make you feel better? Making out.

ERYNNE: Shut up.

NEMO: It'd make me feel better.

ERYNNE: What am I gonna do, though?

NEMO: About your parents, I don't know. Can we talk about something else?

ERYNNE: Why are you being a jerk?

NEMO: What do you mean? Every single day I gotta listen to this. Every single day your parents are freaking out on you, and I listen, and I listen all the time, but come on...let's have some fun, we can't do anything about it.

(Pause. Erynne is hurt.)

That upsets you? All right, all right, I'm sorry.

ERYNNE: It's not my fault.

NEMO: Okay.

ERYNNE: Just...you ever wonder how we got this way?

NEMO: What way?

ERYNNE: I don't know—I just—today I was looking in the mirror, and...I remember what I used to look like, when I was a kid, when I felt...cleaner somehow you know? And then I look at me now and it's just...strange to see what's happened to me.

NEMO: What's happened to you?

ERYNNE: I got all mean. I mean, that's kinda it. There's just this—like the air...irritates me, you know? Like all the time I got like tiny little fires exploding on my skin and I just can't ever get peaceful any more, you know?

NEMO: Take a bath.

ERYNNE: Why do I even bother talking to you?

NEMO: Cause I'm sexy.

ERYNNE: Shut up.

NEMO: Seriously, check this out.

(He poses.)

ERYNNE: Nemo, I'm serious. Stop it for a second!

NEMO: You're always serious! That's what your problem is.

ERYNNE: I'm not asking you to tell me what my problem is —

(Trank jumps in carrying bolt clippers. He screams violently. Both of them freak out.)

TRANK: I will eat your flesh!

NEMO: Ah you skank!

(Trank falls into convulsive laughter. Nemo attacks Trank as he laughs.)

TRANK: Ah man that was hilarious! You're like Aaaaah!

ERYNNE: Yeah, gee, I guess when somebody jumps out of the bushes holding a machete I tend to overreact!

TRANK: Does this look like a machete to you? These are bolt clippers, dumb-ass <moron>.

ERYNNE: Piss off. <Shut up>

TRANK: Oh, I'm chopping my way through the forest! Look at me with my machete!

NEMO: What do you have them for?

TRANK: Dude. Check this out. If you go to the back lot behind the hospital they have an entire tank of nitrous there. So I'm thinking, we take Chubb's mini-van, we go to the back, we sever the thing — pop it in the back... we'll be out of our minds for a month.

NEMO: You want to steal a tank of nitrous from the hospital?

TRANK: Dude, yes. I can already feel the brain cells dying, there's gonna be some kind of like...cranial holocaust going on in here, man. Eat nitrous! Dude, I'm gonna be like a vegetable. Ahhh!

ERYNNE: All right, I'm out.

TRANK: What's wrong with you?

ERYNNE: Did you ask Chubb if you could use the mini-van?

TRANK: Nah, I just took it. What? She lets me use it all the time.

NEMO: I think we'd better think this one through a little better, Trank.

TRANK: Dude, it's a perfect plan.

(Erynne speaks to the audience.)

ERYNNE: Trank's real name was Joseph Ritello. He got the name Trank because he liked to fantasize about horse tranquilizers.

TRANK: Dude. It hits you so fast you gotta have someone next to you to take the pipe out of your hands so you don't burn yourself with it.

ERYNNE: Not that he had ever smoked horse tranquilizers, he just talked about it every day. Trank didn't go to school with the rest of us; he attended Mt. Zion Christian Academy. Which, to hear him tell it, is where he learned all of his criminal tendencies. It's rare to actually come across a person with no morals whatsoever, but Trank was one of those people. Absolutely soulless. His parents were hard-core. They were the kind of people who would go and protest evolution being taught in the schools—I mean, like they had the picket signs already written up in the garage for when they went a marching. So, they raised Trank. And Trank raised hell. I really liked the guy.

(Lights switch back to her bedroom. There's a KNOCK on the door.)

ERYNNE'S FATHER: Erynne?

(No response.)

Are you in there?

(No response. He KNOCKS again.)

If this thing is locked, so help me I'm gonna —

✳ *(He opens the door and enters, looking around. He sees a lump in the bed. He sighs heavily and sits down next to it, putting his hand on its hip.)*

All right, look, you gotta understand that I'm trying to do what's best for you. And uh...sometimes those are difficult choices...so...have you taken a shower recently? Um...anyway, just know that...I love you. Okay?

SCOOTER: *(From underneath the covers:)* I love you too.

(Pause.)

ERYNNE'S FATHER: All right then.

(He gets up and leaves. Lights switch from them to Travis, still staring at the telephone. Finally, it rings. JESSIE, 14, Kimberly's little sister, is on the line.)

JESSIE: Is Travis there?

TRAVIS: Yeah, this is Travis.

JESSIE: Hey.

TRAVIS: Who's this?

JESSIE: Jessie. I'm Kimberly's sister.

TRAVIS: Oh! Hey um —

JESSIE: She wants you to come over.

TRAVIS: Really?

JESSIE: Sure. She thinks you're hot.

TRAVIS: Dude.

JESSIE: She thinks it's totally hot when you mow the lawn.

TRAVIS: No way.

JESSIE: So are you coming over?

(Travis hangs up and runs next door. Jessie is at the door.)

All right, all right, shh—come downstairs.

(Jessie leads Travis into a darkened area.)

All right, stay here, I'm gonna go get her.

TRAVIS: At this point, if I had any sense, I would start to get a bad feeling. But I didn't have any sense, and my stomach was doing somersaults.

(The lights change. Jessie and her gang of little friends, KALLIE, LILY, MORGAN, and DANICA slowly emerge. They look at Travis strangely.)

Hey.

(They laugh.)

KALLIE: *(Mimicking him:)* Hey.

TRAVIS: So uh...what's up?

KALLIE: How's that chest hair coming?

(All the girls giggle.)

TRAVIS: What?

KALLIE: Jessie says you're trying to grow chest hair.

DANICA: You wanna play spin the bottle?

TRAVIS: How old are you? Twelve? I'm seventeen.

DANICA: I'm not twelve. I'm thirteen. Are you scared?

KALLIE: When was the last time you kissed a girl?

TRAVIS: Like, the police will bust down the door and haul me off to jail.

DANICA: Don't you think love is worth it?

KALLIE: Do you love Kimberly?

MORGAN: He totally does.

TRAVIS: No.

KALLIE: Why are you over here then?

MORGAN: Cause he loves Kimberly!

DANICA: She doesn't even like you.

KALLIE: Yeah, she's not all that impressed by the chest hair.

(They all laugh again.)

MORGAN: What do you think about Jessie?

KALLIE: Do you think Jessie's hot?

DANICA: She thinks you're hot.

KALLIE: Shut up! You weren't supposed to tell her that!

DANICA: Whatever.

KALLIE: She's gonna kill you.

TRAVIS: You know what guys—if Kimberly's not here, then you know what—I'm gonna take off—

KALLIE: No no no she's here.

DANICA: She's coming right down.

(The girls laugh again.)

MORGAN: Sit down.

TRAVIS: No thanks.

MORGAN: Sit down or we're gonna come over to your house.

KALLIE: We're totally coming over to your house.

DANICA: We're gonna ring the doorbell at like three in the morning.

KALLIE: We totally know where you live.

TRAVIS: That's nice, guys.

(He tries to leave. Kallie grabs him.)

KALLIE: No wait wait—

DANICA: She's coming right down.

(The girls giggle again.)

MORGAN: What radio station do you listen to?

TRAVIS: All right, you know what—

DANICA: Do you listen to 105.1?

MORGAN: He totally does.

KALLIE: He does not. 98.5.

(Jessie comes back down, having changed clothes and put on a lot of makeup.)

JESSIE: You know what, I can't find her.

TRAVIS: Well just tell her—

KALLIE: That you love her?

DANICA: Shut up!

TRAVIS: All right, you guys have a nice night.

JESSIE: Where are you going?

TRAVIS: I'm going home—okay—

JESSIE: You know Kimberly doesn't have a date for homecoming yet—

KALLIE: Oh! You should totally ask her to homecoming!

DANICA: Yeah, that's gonna work.

MORGAN: He should.

DANICA: You're retarded.

MORGAN: Unnnh.

DANICA: Shut up.

TRAVIS: I should really go home.

KALLIE: What are you gonna do there?

MORGAN: You got a hot date tonight?

TRAVIS: No.

KALLIE: Then stay here.

JESSIE: You know what, Kimberly just ran to the store, she's gonna be right back.

TRAVIS: Really?

JESSIE: Uh huh. Stick around for her.

(Pause. He considers it.)

TRAVIS: All right.

(He sits down. Lights shift. Erynne is sneaking into her house late at night. Her Father is laying in wait. She tries to make it around the corner but he flips on the lights.)

ERYNNE: Ah!

ERYNNE'S FATHER: Sit down.

ERYNNE: Dad—

ERYNNE'S FATHER: Sit down.

(She sits.)

ERYNNE'S FATHER: Bring me your coat.

ERYNNE: You just told me to sit down.

(He flips over a piece of furniture.)

ERYNNE'S FATHER: Don't get smart with me!

(Erynne cringes.)

Get your coat.

(Erynne goes to the closet, brings back her coat. Her Father snatches it from her. He begins rifling through it.)

ERYNNE: Hey!

ERYNNE'S FATHER: Shut up.

(Erynne shuts up. Her Father dumps everything out of her pockets – he finds cigarettes, three lighters, a baggie filled with something organic, a condom, etc... He lays each thing out on the table.)

Cigarettes. One lighter. Two lighters. Three lighters. *(He gets to the baggie:)* Which one of your friends are you getting this from?

(She doesn't say anything.)

Which one. Your boyfriend. Him? You're gonna talk to me or you're gonna talk to the police, you got it?

ERYNNE: I didn't get it from him.

ERYNNE'S FATHER: Who then? *(He leans in again:)* All right listen to me. You may not think so, but this is dangerous. This destroys your brain. And you ain't got that much to start with.

ERYNNE: *(Under her breath:)* I'm still smarter than you.

ERYNNE'S FATHER: What was that?

ERYNNE: I'm smarter than you.

(Her Father grabs her by the shoulder.)

ERYNNE'S FATHER: You know what I think about you right now?

ERYNNE: I got a pretty good idea.

ERYNNE'S FATHER: You're lucky I don't throw you through the wall. You know when I think about what I raised for a daughter it makes me sick.

ERYNNE: Can we please talk when you're not drunk out of your mind?

(He explodes in anger, shaking her.)

ERYNNE'S FATHER: You got some nerve! You think I'm an alcoholic?! Is that what you tell people?! When you're running around with those drug addicts? You think I don't know what you do? You know what's gonna happen to you! You're gonna end up on the street—you got no ambition, you got nothing.

(Short pause.)

ERYNNE: Dad—

ERYNNE'S FATHER: I want you out of my house. I want you gone. *(He pushes her:)* Get that garbage out of your room. See how well you do living on your own.

(The lights change back to the basement. Very late at night now. Everyone is still downstairs. Danica has fallen asleep.)

KALLIE: She's asleep. Shhhh...

(Kallie begins to pile pillows on top of Danica. The others help.)

TRAVIS: But like I'm saying—you gotta...realize, you know, life—

JESSIE: Yeah.

TRAVIS: Here's the thing: my brother—you know, he thinks he's a big shot just because he's a marine, you know? And I mean, that's cool and all—but—

MORGAN: He's a marine?

TRAVIS: Yeah.

MORGAN: Wow.

TRAVIS: Okay, that doesn't like...you know in my family, my parents are miserable. They drive each other nuts, and my Dad is like totally running around on my Mom—and that's just kind of the way it's been for years, you know?

LILY: I think about death all the time.

(Pause. People stop to look at Lily.)

You wanna hear a poem I wrote?

(The girls nod.)

I see darkness all around me
I feel the cold grip of black pain
The sting of my shattered dreams
Outside, the rain falls on us all.
And I scream quietly from the corner.

JESSIE: Wow.

LILY: Did you guys like it?

MORGAN: You should totally make that a song.

(Kimberly comes down the stairs. Everyone freezes. She looks at Travis. Pause.)

KIMBERLY: What are you doing here?

TRAVIS: Hey.

KIMBERLY: It's two o' clock in the morning, what are you doing in my house? With my little sister?

TRAVIS: I was uh...I was waiting for you actually.

(He gets up from the floor where he was sitting.)

KIMBERLY: Do Mom and Dad know he's over here?

JESSIE: We're going out.

TRAVIS: What?

KIMBERLY: Are you kidding me?

TRAVIS: Hey — whoah — no — she's lying —

JESSIE: I don't want to lie any more, Travis.

TRAVIS: Hey wait no —

KIMBERLY: This is disgusting.

(She leaves, Travis races after her. Outside.)

TRAVIS: Kimberly —

KIMBERLY: You're a pervert.

TRAVIS: She's making that up — she called me and said you were home —

KIMBERLY: Well obviously I wasn't.

TRAVIS: Right. Yeah, I should've picked up on that a little sooner. But — look — I'm not going out with your sister — come on — she's got a crush on me or something.

(Kimberly looks at him.)

I came over here...because...do you have a date for homecoming?

KIMBERLY: What?

TRAVIS: Um...would you like to go to homecoming with me?

(Pause. Travis turns to address the audience.)

This is the point in the movie of my life where my character is able to come up with an unexpected burst of eloquence, and is in fact so eloquent that the girl has no choice but to fall in love with the hero, even though she's a lot hotter and more popular than him and really doesn't even know he exists. So, my speech, in the movie version, went something like this: *(Back to her:)* I think about you all the time. And I think about me being with you. And I think about these guys you've been with: Greg, and Sam, and that other guy who was twenty-two years old and still lived at home. And I watch you every day, and I know that they've been awful to you, I know that they've used you, and cheated on you, and treated you like dirt, and that makes me sick inside because I know that you're a diamond, and you should be treated tenderly and cleanly and with respect, and I would be the guy who would open doors for you and pull out your chair and bring you flowers unexpectedly — and I would do my best to make you happy, to share my inside with you, to share my thoughts with you, to hear your thoughts and to listen to you, to really listen, so that I knew who you were on the inside instead of just the outside like these jerks you've been with. I would be the guy that would make sure you got home okay, I would massage your shoulders when you were stressed. I would help you with your homework when it was hard — and I would thank God for the joy you would bring into my life. And if you want that kind of guy instead of some creep then please, for all that is holy, go with me to the homecoming dance. *(To the audience:)* It came out something like this: *(To her:)* Cause um...

KIMBERLY: Travis. I think we should just be friends. Okay?

TRAVIS: Okay.

KIMBERLY: You gotta go.

TRAVIS: See you tomorrow.

KIMBERLY: Good night.

TRAVIS: Night.

> *(He leaves. Stops, turns around to look at her. Then keeps going. She enters the house. Inside Travis' house, his FATHER waits, pacing like a caged animal.)*

TRAVIS' FATHER: Hey Travis.

TRAVIS: What are you doing up so late?

TRAVIS' FATHER: What are you doing out?

TRAVIS: I was just next door.

TRAVIS' FATHER: Doing what?

TRAVIS: Hanging out with a bunch of middle school girls.

> *(His Father looks at him strangely.)*

TRAVIS: They were surprisingly cool.

TRAVIS' FATHER: Travis. *(He's about to give some fatherly advice, but isn't quite sure how to approach the subject:)* I know you've been having difficulty with girls your own age but that doesn't mean you have to slide down the ladder. You know what I'm saying?

TRAVIS: Is Mom up?

> *(Pause.)*

TRAVIS' FATHER: I'm gonna leave your mother. *(Pause.)* After her birthday I'm gonna go out to California. And I'm not coming back.

TRAVIS: California?

TRAVIS' FATHER: Yeah. So—um... You're gonna be a man—you're gonna graduate from high school here, and you gotta be strong about this. And you gotta help her, okay, because she's not gonna take it well. Especially with Nick away. Okay? You're her baby.

TRAVIS: Have you talked about this with her?

TRAVIS' FATHER: There's some things you just gotta do. And one of these days you're going to have to take a chance too. Now that little heart attack I had last year really got me thinking, and it got me thinking about my life and the direction it took. And I'll say this to you: Cause maybe one day you'll think about this and understand what I'm talking about. If you don't watch it, life sneaks up on you. If you don't make things happen for yourself, things will happen to you, and then you've got no choice. But you can't live life afraid of hurting someone. Cause then it's all spent and then you've got nothing really to show for it. There was a time when I thought I was going to change the world, but you get so busy living that you never make it to what you dreamed you would be. And that's my lesson to you. Don't wait. Don't wait thirty years to start going after what you want. *(Pause.)* Unless it's the middle school girls, in which case you gotta wait a couple of years. But that's okay.

(Lights shift. Morning in Erynne's house. ERYNNE's MOTHER and Father are sitting at the table. Erynne enters.)

ERYNNE'S MOTHER: Sit down.

(Erynne sits.)

ERYNNE: I'm sorry.

ERYNNE'S MOTHER: Your father and I have talked about it. And um...

(She looks to him.)

ERYNNE'S FATHER: We've tried.

ERYNNE: You have not.

ERYNNE'S MOTHER: Erynne.   We need to have a polite conversation about this. Okay?

ERYNNE: All right.

ERYNNE'S FATHER: We set rules for your protection.   It is our responsibility to — and we have tried — to enforce them, okay? In order to keep you safe.

ERYNNE: I'm not safe.

ERYNNE'S FATHER: I know you're not —

ERYNNE: And that's got more to do with you than me.

ERYNNE'S FATHER: Okay. Gail?

ERYNNE'S MOTHER: What your father is trying to say is that in order to live here you have to be willing to...cooperate, okay? You always have the freedom to refuse to do what we tell you, but if you do that long enough, there are consequences. Okay? *(Short pause.)* You endanger us. By bringing drugs into the house — by being involved with gangs —

ERYNNE: My friends are not a gang!

ERYNNE'S MOTHER: Who knows when one of them is going to go crazy and take a gun —

ERYNNE: You don't even know what a gang is!

ERYNNE'S MOTHER: Erynne, I'm trying to speak to you like a person. I'd appreciate it if you didn't scream at me.

ERYNNE: Okay.

ERYNNE'S MOTHER: It tears me up inside every time I see you. You know that? I look at you—and I mean, just...your appearance...your appearance says that you don't like who you are.

ERYNNE: Cause I wear black?

ERYNNE'S MOTHER: I used to like who you were. I don't like you now. And what hurts me is you don't want me to like you. You deliberately try to be like this. I...love you, Erynne. But we don't love what you've become. And we have tried for two years to change that, and, I think it's time to face the reality that you're not going to change. Because you don't want to change.

ERYNNE: That's right.

ERYNNE'S MOTHER: Then we don't want you to be our daughter.

(Pause. Her Father holds on to her Mother. She starts to cry.)

ERYNNE: *(Breaking:)* What...does that mean?

ERYNNE'S MOTHER: You have to leave.

ERYNNE'S FATHER: We've tried...treatment and that doesn't work cause you don't want it to, so...so we can't do this any more. So you need to go.

ERYNNE'S MOTHER: I love you.

(She makes a move to reach out, but her Father holds her back. Lights shift.)

TRAVIS: *(To the audience:)* My mother's birthday came and went but he didn't leave. He stayed. And he was miserable. And I think he was having an affair somewhere cause he'd be gone for long stretches at a time, but I didn't really know for sure. So every day I came home wondering if my Dad was still going to be there. And looking at my Mom and wondering if I should tell her what he told me.

(Lights shift to the kitchen. Travis is helping TRAVIS' MOTHER make dinner.)

TRAVIS' MOTHER: Do you want corn on the cob or potato salad?

TRAVIS: Potato salad.

TRAVIS' MOTHER: Too bad. I already started the corn on the cob.

TRAVIS: Then why'd you ask?

TRAVIS' MOTHER: Habit. Do you want cole slaw or baked beans?

TRAVIS: Either.

TRAVIS' MOTHER: Okay.

TRAVIS: Mom?

TRAVIS' MOTHER: What?

(Pause.)

TRAVIS: Where's Dad?

TRAVIS' MOTHER: He's running errands. He should be home soon. *(Pause. She stops to look at him:)* What's wrong?

TRAVIS: Nothing. I'm just worried about global warming. Do you really think the icecaps are going to melt?

TRAVIS' MOTHER: I don't know honey. I try not to think about it. The world has been here for a long time and every couple of years they come up and say this new thing is going to be the worst disaster in human history. And you know what? Life goes on. So I wouldn't spend too much time worrying about it.

TRAVIS: Okay.

TRAVIS' MOTHER: When I was growing up it was nuclear war. And trust me, that's a lot scarier than having hot summers or the sea level going up a foot or two. That was a real problem, trust me.

TRAVIS: Yeah.

TRAVIS' MOTHER: I was always sure the end was just around the corner. Of course, it wasn't.

TRAVIS: What if it really was just around the corner? What if we're at the end?

TRAVIS' MOTHER: Then end of what?

TRAVIS: The end of the world.

TRAVIS' MOTHER: We're not at the end of the world.

TRAVIS: What if something horrible happened? And then um...and then...what if that something was kinda small—like—

TRAVIS' MOTHER: Like what?

TRAVIS: Like what if Dad left?

(Pause. They look at each other.)

TRAVIS' MOTHER: What did he tell you?

(Pause. Travis' Father enters carrying two bags of groceries.)

TRAVIS' FATHER: Hey Travis, go get the rest of the bags out of the trunk.

(He sets the groceries down and begins unloading them.)

TRAVIS: Okay, Dad.

(He leaves. Travis' Mother and Father look at each other.)

For many years I wondered what they said to each other when I was getting the bags out of the trunk. But that was the last day they were together. My father left for California that night—he packed some of his stuff together and took the car— And while I was gone, I imagine it went something like this:

TRAVIS' MOTHER: When were you planning on telling me you were thinking of leaving me?

TRAVIS' FATHER: Terri, I—

TRAVIS' MOTHER: Have I gotten too old?

TRAVIS' FATHER: No.

TRAVIS' MOTHER: Was there something I should've done?

TRAVIS' FATHER: My heart isn't in it.

TRAVIS' MOTHER: In what?

TRAVIS' FATHER: In this. In this family.

TRAVIS' MOTHER: How long has it been like that?

TRAVIS' FATHER: Since the beginning.

TRAVIS' MOTHER: Your heart hasn't been in it for twenty-three years? *(Pause.)* And you never felt like telling that to me?

TRAVIS' FATHER: I didn't want to hurt you.

(Pause. She sits down. Travis comes back in with the groceries. Neither of his parents says anything. He begins unloading groceries.)

TRAVIS: Do these go in the fridge?

TRAVIS' MOTHER: ...yeah.

(She leaves. Travis' Father remains for a moment, then heads out in the opposite direction.)

ERYNNE: I spent four days living in Chubb's `87 Plymouth Voyager. Powder Blue. Like the color of the sky. She managed to sneak me a couple of blankets out of her house, cause it got really cold at night, and even though I wanted to, we couldn't run the car at night so there was no heat. And I would wake up at seven and hide until her parents left for work, then I would sneak into Chubb's house and take a quick shower so I could go to school. Not that I really wanted to go to school, but at least things there were kinda normal. Chubb's parents were not going to be cool with some druggie girl living out of her car, and on the fourth day her Dad snuck outside to smoke a cigarette and he spotted me. So that was the end of living with Chubb. Trank lived with his Mom, but she was freaking crazy, so I couldn't really stay there; Nemo was my first choice of course —

NEMO: I don't think so.

ERYNNE: Oh come on. Just for a little while. It'll be fun.

NEMO: Erynne —

ERYNNE: I'll live in your closet.

NEMO: No.

ERYNNE: I'm serious, I'll like hide in there and no one will ever know I'm here. I'm real quiet, I'll just make like, little growling noises when I want some food.

NEMO: Why don't you just go home?

ERYNNE: They kicked me out.

NEMO: Well go back and apologize or whatever — they have to take you back in. They can't just kick you out —

ERYNNE: They said if I go back again they're going to hand me over to Juvie or something —

NEMO: They are not.

ERYNNE: I can't go back there.

NEMO: They can't just turn you out on the street — go to the police —

ERYNNE: Yeah, that's gonna happen.

NEMO: Well you can't stay here.

ERYNNE: Why not?

NEMO: You just can't.

ERYNNE: I'll be quiet —

NEMO: Erynne! Listen to me... You cannot stay here. I don't want you to stay here.

(Pause. She's hurt.)

I didn't mean it like that —

ERYNNE: Yeah you did.

(She starts to leave.)

NEMO: Erynne.

ERYNNE: Fine I'll sleep on the street. That's what you want anyway.

NEMO: That's not what I — You're being ridiculous.

(She spins on him.)

ERYNNE: What! Why don't you want me here?!

NEMO: I didn't think we were that serious—

ERYNNE: What the heck does that mean?

NEMO: Well what if we broke up?

ERYNNE: We're not gonna break up!

NEMO: But what if we did? What would you do?

ERYNNE: Stop getting off the subject!

NEMO: You'd probably fall down and die. I mean, look at you, we've only been going out five months and already you're like, we're gonna get married or whatever, or you want to move in with me—

ERYNNE: I was kicked out of my house! This isn't a vacation!

NEMO: And you keep pushing and pushing for us to do all this stuff together all the time—I can't be there all the time for you, okay? I know that you want me to, but you can't lean on me every second of every day, and if you were living here then that's all it would be—all the time, okay, you just...you just...you need help, that's all, and it's not something I can give to you.

ERYNNE: So basically what you're saying is that you want all the physical stuff without having to listen to me talk. Is that it?

NEMO: No.

ERYNNE: Screw you.

NEMO: That's not what I'm saying!

(She leaves. Erynne crosses the stage to Chubb as the lights shift.)

ERYNNE: This is totally a bad idea.

CHUBB: Just for a week. Then we'll figure something out.

ERYNNE: He's really weird.

CHUBB: I'm aware of that. Have you met his family?

ERYNNE: No.

(*Chubb rings the doorbell. ROHAN, Scooter's older brother, opens it. Rohan has long, flowing black hair and wears a cape of some kind. He's absolutely terrifying.*)

ROHAN: Yes?

ERYNNE: Hi. Um...is Scooter home?

ROHAN: He dwells within.

(*Rohan sweeps aside his cape to let them enter.*)

ROHAN: Scooter! Your companions have arrived!

(*Erynne and Chubb sit down on a couch. Rohan sits opposite them.*)

CHUBB: Hi.

ERYNNE: Hey.

(*Rohan simply stares at them.*)

CHUBB: So...um...it's just you and your brother living here?

ROHAN: Our sister as well.

CHUBB: Oh! Cool—

(*She nudges Erynne a little.*)

ERYNNE: What?

CHUBB: How old's your sister?

ROHAN: Many moons.

CHUBB: Right. So what's your name again?

ROHAN: I am known as Rohan.

CHUBB: Like in the Lord of the Rings?

(He glares at them.)

Sorry.

ESMERELDA: *(Offstage:)* Billy! Get your butt back in here and clean up the dishes!

ROHAN: My servants shall do it!

ESMERELDA: *(Offstage:)* Don't make me come in there and slap you!

ROHAN: I must away.

(He gets up with a sweep of his cloak.)

ESMERELDA: *(Offstage:)* This is gross, Billy!

(They can be heard arguing offstage.)

ERYNNE: I'm not staying here.

CHUBB: He's totally fine

ERYNNE: What are you talking about? He makes Scooter look like the well-adjusted one! I don't even want to meet their sister!

(Offstage she shrieks something particularly vile.)

CHUBB: Erynne. They will take you in.

ERYNNE: I'm going to be infected with whatever brand of crazy lives here. I mean, look at this gene pool. No wonder their parents split.

CHUBB: Just for a week, okay? Then I'll get something figured out.

(Scooter enters.)

SCOOTER: You found me.

CHUBB: Yes, we tracked you down.

SCOOTER: You met Rohan.

ERYNNE: Yeah. He's a treat.

SCOOTER: Be careful. He's a warlock.

ERYNNE: All right, it was nice talking to you Scooter —

(She gets up to leave. Chubb grabs her.)

CHUBB: Scooter. Erynne got kicked out of her house by her demonic parents — can she stay here? She'll be really quiet.

ERYNNE: Actually, don't worry about it —

SCOOTER: We have an extra room.

CHUBB: Oh. See?

SCOOTER: It's haunted.

CHUBB: That's fine. She loves haunted stuff.

SCOOTER: We've been trying to capture the ghost for many months now — but it is eluding us.

CHUBB: Well, yeah, you know, that happens. Erynne?

ERYNNE: I can't pay any rent or anything.

SCOOTER: We get checks from the government.

CHUBB: Hey all right!

ERYNNE: What do you get checks from the government for?

SCOOTER: I think it has something to do with mental health.

ERYNNE: Makes sense.

CHUBB: So are you gonna stay?

ERYNNE: Sure.

SCOOTER: Let's have a party. We'll invite all our friends.

ERYNNE: Maybe later. Hey—hey...Scooter, thanks.

SCOOTER: Glad to help.

(Lights shift. Erynne addresses the audience.)

ERYNNE: So then there was Esmerelda. Based on my impressions of Scooter and his lovely brother Rohan, I had a mental picture of Esmerelda that was somewhere between a hard-core cultist and a teletubbie. I kind of imagined her wobbling out of the kitchen, lit-up from within by some translucent screen filled with flashing images, all the while spouting off about the power of magic and her own spells which she would cast upon the evil-doers. The reality, however, was a little off.

(ESMERELDA, 23 sits on the couch next to Erynne. She seems completely normal in comparison to her siblings.)

ESMERELDA: You want some tea?

ERYNNE: No thanks.

ESMERELDA: You're friends with Scooter?

ERYNNE: I don't know that I'd say friends.

ESMERELDA: What would you say you are then?

ERYNNE: Basically acquaintances who are friendly.

ESMERELDA: Right. You may have noticed that my brothers are a little strange.

ERYNNE: Yes. Yes I have.

ESMERELDA: We're really not all that related.

ERYNNE: Oh.

ESMERELDA: They're adopted.

ERYNNE: Oh. You guys got a great deal on that.

ESMERELDA: They were kind of left on our doorstep.

ERYNNE: Oh. That was a nice present.

ESMERELDA: And my parents took them in.

ERYNNE: Where are they now?

ESMERELDA: Well...about the time that Billy started calling himself Rohan and holding séances in our backyard, they found more and more excuses to be out of the house. Until finally, they just stopped coming back.

(Lights switch. Travis is in his bedroom, on the phone with Nick.)

NICK: What's up?

TRAVIS: Nothing.

NICK: You got a girl yet?

TRAVIS: I asked out Kimberly.

NICK: Kimberly who?

TRAVIS: Our neighbor.

NICK: Are you kidding me? You dumb-ass <moron>.

TRAVIS: What?

NICK: She's not gonna go out with you. Be serious.

TRAVIS: Why not?

NICK: Because she's hot, that's why. You need to find some ugly girl to go out with. Find a fat one. They appreciate guys who think they might be gay.

TRAVIS: I'm not gay.

NICK: No, that's cool, you don't need to convince me. I know. It's the girls you gotta convince.

TRAVIS: I'm not gay.

NICK: Fine. So she said no, right?

TRAVIS: She said she wanted to be friends.

NICK: Uh-huh. And has she done a lot of friendly things since then?

TRAVIS: No.

NICK: She doesn't want to be friends. She wants you to never talk to her again. You should go after her little sister —

TRAVIS: She's like thirteen.

NICK: So? She'd go out with you. That's about the best you can hope for right now. Go down to the middle school. Sniff around a little bit.

TRAVIS: You're disgusting.

NICK: Whatever. You been working out?

TRAVIS: A little.

NICK: No you haven't. That's all I do here. You know I can bench two sixty now?

TRAVIS: Really.

NICK: Seriously.

TRAVIS: So...uh...how is it?

NICK: Sucks. The whole place smells like boiling garbage. It's a hundred and twenty degrees today. You know what they got here for natural resources? Sand. It doesn't rain here, sand just blows in outta the desert — sucks. Just as soon go home.

TRAVIS: I thought you were gonna make it a resort community.

NICK: Right. Yeah well that plan has been put on hold until the whole place stops reeking like a dead dog that's been lying in a pile of filth for two weeks. Why anyone lives here I don't know. The best thing to do would probably be burn the whole place down and start over. Put some decent roads in — find some water, I don't know, put in a golf course. We went golfing the other day.

TRAVIS: You did not.

NICK: They got this course here — Saddam's private course — so of course they opened it up to Americans, and we're out there — the thing hasn't been watered in a year so it's like, this brown, ragged mess, right, and there are rocks everywhere and the whole thing sucks — like, how are you gonna golf in this, you know? So we're out there, me and a couple of other guys, and we're just hacking away at our balls — next thing you know, I go to hit the ball, and boom! Mortar shell lands about two blocks from us. I'm not kidding you. And I'm like, these dumb bastards <idiots> are trying to blow up their own golf course — so I start waving my clubs and I'm like, over here, retards!

TRAVIS: What did they do?

NICK: Nothing. They fire one shot then they gotta move cause we track `em down.

TRAVIS: Oh. So...um...how're you doing?

NICK: I miss America, man.

TRAVIS: Really?

NICK: Oh dude, let me tell you. You don't know how good you got it over there. People around the rest of the world — I mean it's like medieval times over here—these people, you know, they worry about how they're gonna eat, they're worried about how many children they got and if they should get rid of some—and all the time their minds are filled with madness and they hate our guts, not all of `em, not all of `em, but I pass kids on the street, ten, eleven-year old kids, and they just stare at you, you know? They see the uniform, they see the armored vehicle, and they go home and live in rubble and they want us dead, man. For no reason. They want us dead because they want someone to pay for what's happened to them. And man, it's like, you wanna reason with them, you wanna say, 'hey, you know why things are such a crazy mess right now?' it's cause of you, it's cause of your family, it's cause of the people blowing things up left and right trying to kill as many people as possible. That's why life is misery, you know? So you go through that, every day you go through that, kids, girls, spit at you. They got eyes like coal, they got voices like they're on fire, and that's every day—every day you see that, for no reason at all. We live like kings in America, Travis. Kings.

TRAVIS: When are you comin' home?

NICK: Six months. That's what they say anyway. Hopefully things will keep quiet for a little while and I can get out faster. How're Mom and Dad?

(Pause.)

TRAVIS: Fine.

NICK: Yeah?

TRAVIS: Yeah, they're fine.

NICK: Good. Tell `em I love `em, all right?

TRAVIS: Yeah.

NICK: All right—and stop being such a wuss.

TRAVIS: I got it.

NICK: I'll talk to you later.

TRAVIS: Hey Nick?

NICK: Yeah?

TRAVIS: Stay safe out there okay?

NICK: No problem.

(He hangs up. Lights shift, but remain on Travis. Erynne is in a solitary room, looking around, quite disturbed. In the far distance, chanting is heard.)

TRAVIS: I laid awake that night—

ERYNNE: I listened to the sounds of the highway that ran past the front door. In the haunted room I found myself in, and I thought about all these things—that I wasn't good enough, that I wasn't going to make it, that life was just too hard—

TRAVIS: I heard my mother downstairs, she was still up, she was up still going through those albums, wondering what had happened to her family. Was it all a lie? Was all that time we spent together a fraud?

ERYNNE: I want to burn down the world. I want to burn it up—explode, fire the whole thing, just to let it know that I'm here, and say that I am better than this. This is not me. This wasted, messed-up girl is not all that I am—I am more than this. I am a person—I am a light.

TRAVIS: I walked down the stairs—it was a warm fall night—we had all the windows open and you could smell the heat as it seeped in from the outside, and the soft purr of the crickets, and the flutter of insects against the lights—and here we are, so safe—

ERYNNE: So angry, those self-satisfied bastards, just because I don't fit into what they think I should be, just because I'm not exactly like everyone else. I should tear out their hearts for this.

TRAVIS: I thought about my brother on the other side of the world. In the middle of some blinding heat, walking down some shattered road where people had no hope, where they toiled and they burned and they were close to death at all times, and I thought about my life here, in between the Wal-Mart and the McDonald's and the ribbons of highways cutting through the night —

ERYNNE: My sister was the same as me. She was just like me. She lived, she burned, she was burning all the time —

TRAVIS: But none of us are safe — my father proved that —

(Travis reaches his mother. Erynne gets up from the bed and begins walking.)

ERYNNE: So I went out for a walk on the side of the highway. Down the road, not even really caring where I walked to. And sometimes cars would flash their brights at me, sometimes they would slow down, just to see this girl alongside the highway, in the ditch, walking.

TRAVIS: And I think about America, and how we were once expected to all put ourselves in danger, and now we don't, now most of us are fat and lazy and cozy, like babies, and maybe the right thing to do is go into the army as soon I graduate, to pay in, like Nick, to be strong, like Nick, to find myself, like he did — *(To his Mother now:)* Mom?

TRAVIS' MOTHER: You're up?

TRAVIS: You should go to sleep.

TRAVIS' MOTHER: I can't sleep.

TRAVIS: It's gonna be okay.

TRAVIS' MOTHER: You don't know that.

(He tries to pull her up. Short pause.)

ERYNNE: I walk and I walk and I find myself going somewhere. And I look at the stretch of road, at the curve of it, the twist, and I know where I am. We put a cross here six years ago. When Dierdre lost her grip, when she flew through the air, when she slid across the pavement. She landed over there.

DIERDRE: Hey Erynne.

ERYNNE: Hi.

DIERDRE: How ya doing?

ERYNNE: Not good.

DIERDRE: You look like a mess.

ERYNNE: Sorry.

DIERDRE: Sing something for me. You always had the prettiest voice.

ERYNNE: No thanks.

DIERDRE: What's the matter?

(Erynne sits down.)

ERYNNE: You wouldn't understand.

DIERDRE: Just cause I look like a thirteen year-old doesn't mean I am.

ERYNNE: Why'd you do it?

DIERDRE: Fun.

ERYNNE: Really?

DIERDRE: I bet you wish I had some big cosmic reason, like I was bored with the ordinariness of life. But really, it just seemed fun at the time. Course I didn't think he was going to get up to forty miles an hour, but that's really his cross to bear at this point.

ERYNNE: What's it like? Dying?

DIERDRE: Thinking about making the trip?

ERYNNE: *(Quietly:)* No.

DIERDRE: Then I can't tell you.

ERYNNE: Are you in heaven?

DIERDRE: Do you want me to be in heaven? Would it make things better for you?

ERYNNE: I don't know.

DIERDRE: I can't give you that answer.

ERYNNE: Why not?

DIERDRE: Really I'm just a figment of your imagination.

ERYNNE: Oh.

DIERDRE: At least I think so. I'm not really all that sure.

ERYNNE: Dierdre?

DIERDRE: Yeah?

ERYNNE: Was it this hard for you?

DIERDRE: No.

(Switch over to Travis and his Mother. The phone rings.)

TRAVIS: A little late.

(Travis' Mother answers the phone.)

TRAVIS' MOTHER: Hello? This is Terri.

(She sits down slowly.)

TRAVIS: Mom?

(She drops the phone.)

Mom?

(MUSIC. Meatloaf. "For Crying Out Loud.")

Are you okay?

(Erynne and DIERDRE are together.)

ERYNNE: I miss you.

TRAVIS: What is it?

TRAVIS' MOTHER: Nick.

(End of Act I.)

ACT II

(MUSIC. Erynne is creeping around the outside of her house. Inside, her Mother and Father are on the couch, watching television. She finds her window and tries it. It's locked. She waits outside for a moment, unsure of what to do.)

ERYNNE'S MOTHER: Do we have to watch this show?

ERYNNE'S FATHER: Yes.

ERYNNE'S MOTHER: It's not funny.

ERYNNE'S FATHER: Did I ask you?

ERYNNE'S MOTHER: Gimme the remote control.

ERYNNE'S FATHER: No.

ERYNNE'S MOTHER: Give it to me.

ERYNNE'S FATHER: You don't have to watch TV.

ERYNNE'S MOTHER: Every night we gotta watch this crap. What is so wrong with you that you find Pamela Anderson entertaining?

ERYNNE'S FATHER: She's funny.

ERYNNE'S MOTHER: You just want to stare at her boobs.

ERYNNE'S FATHER: Ah, you got me. We're still watching it.

ERYNNE'S MOTHER: It's stupid.

ERYNNE'S FATHER: Then go in another room. Nobody wants you in here.

ERYNNE'S MOTHER: Fine I'm going in the kitchen.

ERYNNE'S FATHER: That's a good place for you.

ERYNNE'S MOTHER: You know what Brad? Kiss my butt.

ERYNNE'S FATHER: No.

ERYNNE'S MOTHER: Fine. I'll be in the kitchen.

ERYNNE'S FATHER: I heard you the first time.

ERYNNE'S MOTHER: Some day, when you're dying of cancer and you can't talk any more, I'll be there in the hospital room, and you know what I'm gonna do? I'm gonna change the channel to Lifetime and leave it there. You got it? Television for Women. On your deathbed.

ERYNNE'S FATHER: That'll kill me pretty quick.

ERYNNE'S MOTHER: Good. Then I can have the remote.

(She leaves.)

ERYNNE'S FATHER: Hey get me a beer!

ERYNNE'S MOTHER: *(In the kitchen:)* Get your own beer!

(Erynne rings the doorbell.)

ERYNNE'S FATHER: That's the doorbell.

ERYNNE'S MOTHER: Do you think I'm deaf?

ERYNNE'S FATHER: Get it.

ERYNNE'S MOTHER: Yeah that's gonna happen. Get off your own lazy butt and answer the door.

ERYNNE'S FATHER: *(Calling out:)* It's open!

(Erynne opens the door tentatively.)

ERYNNE: Hey.

(They look at her. Pause.)

ERYNNE'S MOTHER: *(Softly:)* What do you want?

(Pause. She stares at them.)

ERYNNE: I wanna come home.

(Her Father signs deeply and looks at her Mother.)

ERYNNE'S FATHER: Um...

ERYNNE'S MOTHER: Do you want something to eat?

ERYNNE: No.

ERYNNE'S FATHER: Why do you wanna come home?

(She shrugs.)

Tell me why.

(Erynne squirms a little bit.)

ERYNNE: I'm sorry.

ERYNNE'S FATHER: That's not a reason.

ERYNNE'S MOTHER: Brad.

ERYNNE'S FATHER: No no, I wanna hear this. If she wants to come back here, she can tell us why. You were pretty eager to leave the first time —

ERYNNE: I was not!

ERYNNE'S FATHER: By your actions, you made it clear that you didn't want to be here.

ERYNNE: I never said that I didn't want to be here!

ERYNNE'S FATHER: If you wanted to be here, you'd follow our rules.

ERYNNE'S MOTHER: Can we turn this stupid show off now?

(She goes for the remote. Erynne's Father takes it and shuts off the television.)

ERYNNE'S FATHER: You understand what I'm saying?

ERYNNE: No.

ERYNNE'S FATHER: Well. Why should I let you come back then?

ERYNNE: I'll be good.

ERYNNE'S FATHER: I don't know that I believe that.

ERYNNE: Well what do you want?!

ERYNNE'S MOTHER: Don't scream.

ERYNNE: You want me to live on the street?!

ERYNNE'S MOTHER: Sweetie, are you —

ERYNNE'S FATHER: Gail.

ERYNNE: Why do you shut her down like that? Why can't you just let her talk? You're such an asshole.

ERYNNE'S FATHER: All right, you know what? It's time for you to go.

(*He gets up from the chair.*)

ERYNNE: Why can't you just let me talk to you?!

ERYNNE'S FATHER: Talk! Go ahead talk! No one's stopping you! Why should I take you back in!?

ERYNNE: Because I —

ERYNNE'S FATHER: When you were here, you didn't respect me, you didn't respect your mother — you and your friends treated this house like your own little drug den, you stole from us, you took money from your mother, you didn't obey our rules, you cussed at us, you skipped school, I've paid fines for you, every day since you were fourteen you've been a complete mess and it hurts me, you understand that? It hurts me because I sit back and think what did I do wrong with you that you're so...vicious and mean and angry, that you are...a blot on this family — it makes me sick to my stomach to look at you and think that you are my only child! You understand that?! You make me sick coming in here dressed like that with your hair all putrid, wearing all that black, with that attitude that the world sucks and that your only role in it is to get what you want and screw everyone else! I'm sick of it! You understand! So you explain to me why on earth I would want you to live under the same roof as me. Why should I spend my money to feed you, to buy you black clothes, to keep you warm, to keep you safe, when all I ever get from you is hate and spit and pain! *(Pause.)* Well?

(Erynne gets up and heads deeper into the house.)

Where are you going?

ERYNNE: I'm gonna get my stuff!

(He grabs her by the arm.)

ERYNNE'S FATHER: What stuff?

ERYNNE: Let go of me!

ERYNNE'S FATHER: What stuff!

ERYNNE'S MOTHER: Brad. Let go of her.

(He looks at her Mother, but doesn't let go.)

Sweetie, what do you need?

ERYNNE: Well I just need to check on some stuff.

ERYNNE'S MOTHER: We went through it, and...

ERYNNE'S FATHER: We got rid of it.

(Pause. Erynne slides away from him and slumps to the ground.)

ERYNNE'S MOTHER: *(To her Father:)* Why did you say that?

ERYNNE'S FATHER: Gail.

ERYNNE: *(Quietly:)* Why...?

ERYNNE'S MOTHER: Well...

ERYNNE: Did you do that immediately? Did you just go through my stuff that night and trash everything? Why would you do that?

ERYNNE'S MOTHER: You have to understand —

ERYNNE: You never thought I was going to come back for it?

ERYNNE'S MOTHER: We saved what we thought was important, okay?

(Erynne's Father shoots her a look. Erynne's Mother tries to touch her on the shoulder, but Erynne jerks away from the contact, slapping at her hand.)

ERYNNE'S FATHER: Erynne. We were looking for drugs.

ERYNNE: I didn't have any. And that doesn't give you a right to destroy my things.

ERYNNE'S FATHER: We needed to be thorough. Now listen —

(She kicks at him.)

All right, time for you to go. Get up.

ERYNNE: I'm not going anywhere.

ERYNNE'S FATHER: Get up.

ERYNNE: Screw you.

ERYNNE'S FATHER: That's it. *(He grabs her roughly and forcibly pulls her to her feet:)* You want me to call the police?

ERYNNE: Go ahead and do it. I'll tell them all about you.

ERYNNE'S FATHER: You're leaving.

ERYNNE: Go ahead, call them. Call the police. I'm gonna report you anyway for throwing me out—you can't just kick me out of the house—that's child abuse— They're gonna put you in jail.

(He's pulled her just about all the way to the door.)

Why do you think I'm messed up, huh? You think I don't know I'm messed up? You think I want to be like this?

(He opens the door and shoves her roughly. She spits in his face. Enraged, he goes to strike her, but stops.)

ERYNNE'S FATHER: Don't come back. You're an animal. You hear me?

(He slams the door. Erynne waits for a second then kicks the door. Erynne's Fasther waits on the other side of it.)

ERYNNE: *(Shouting through the door:)* Mom! Mom! You let him do this! You let him!

(Inside, Erynne's Mother makes a move toward the door, then stops. Outside, Erynne kicks at it again... Slowly, she leaves, not looking back. Lights change. The music of a military band. The MINISTER, middle-aged, steps forward, carrying a bible.)

MINISTER: I had the pleasure of knowing Nicholas for quite a few years. I first met him in his confirmation training when he was thirteen, and I watched him as he matured from a typical thirteen year old boy to a young man of character and strength. And it is an honor to be here today to remember this young man, who gave his life for us. Nicholas died when his vehicle was struck by what is known as an IED, an Improvised Explosive Device. We would call it a roadside bomb. They strike randomly, the young man who built that device did not know him; the young man who planted it in the road would not recognize him. Perhaps had they met under different circumstances, Nicholas and this young man who killed him, would have been friends. I ask myself many questions. I ask the same questions his family asks. Why does God permit war? Why take Nicholas? What purpose does this serve? For as long as humans have had the ability to think they have asked these questions. They ask them now, they asked them in Germany, they asked them on a hill near Jerusalem when another young man gave his life so that his friends might be saved. His name was Jesus Christ. God has made us, on this earth, mortal. From the moment we are born, we are on a path to this day. When the flowers are laid out for us, when our family gathers to remember our soul. Our souls, though, are eternal. That is God's promise. That is why that other young man gave his life. Nicholas is not gone, he lives on in you, and he lives with our Lord in heaven. I know this about the young man. When we send our soldiers off to war, we send our best. I know this to be true about him because I spoke with him before he left—he was not afraid—we send young men who believe in the responsibility of the strong to protect the weak, we send young men who believe in their duty to this country, who believe in honor, and morality, and peace. We do not send killers. We send our sons, and our brothers, and our fathers and even our sisters and daughters and mothers, and all those who would be willing to sacrifice themselves so that those of us here in America, whose memory of war on our own soil is nearly forgotten, so those of us here might keep safe. And whatever you might say about this war, our men that see to its fighting give us hope. And the price for that hope, sadly, is blood. Amen.

(Bagpipe music. The funeral procession gathers. Travis stands with his Mother. Kimberly and Jessie stand nearby, dressed in black. Travis' Father stands opposite them, alone. Others are there as well. Slowly, four MARINES in dress uniform carry a flag-draped coffin onto the stage. They set the coffin down and

remove the flag, folding it ceremonially. One Marine pivots and hands the folded flag to Travis' Mother. Travis' Father walks toward his mother, head down. He puts his hand on her shoulder. Three sharp rifle reports. A Marine in dress uniform plays Taps on the bugle. Other members of the funeral approach Travis' Mother and Father to offer their condolences. Travis backs away from them, watching. After a moment, Jessie comes over to him.)

JESSIE: Hey.

TRAVIS: Hi.

(She hesitates for a moment, then gives him a hug. Lights shift back to their home. Travis' Mother is sitting down, nearly catatonic. Travis sits near her. After a moment, Travis' Fasther knocks tentatively on the door, then enters.)

TRAVIS' FATHER: Can I come in?

(No real response from Travis' Mother. His Father steps in.)

TRAVIS' FATHER: You gotta think the timing of this is pretty bad, huh?

TRAVIS' MOTHER: How's California?

TRAVIS' FATHER: It's all right. I'm renting a little place near the beach. The water's pretty cold yet, you know? I tried to go swimming the other day and I nearly froze to death.

TRAVIS' MOTHER: You got a job?

TRAVIS' FATHER: Still looking. *(Short pause.)* How're you doing, Travis?

(No response.)

Yeah. It's pretty bad. Umm... His commanding officer said some pretty nice things.

TRAVIS: That was his drill sergeant.

TRAVIS' FATHER: Right.

TRAVIS: His commanding officer is still over there.

TRAVIS' FATHER: Yeah. That makes sense. Uh... Travis? Do you think uh...you could let your mother and me talk...for a little bit?

(Travis looks to his Mother.)

TRAVIS' MOTHER: It's okay.

TRAVIS: All right.

(Travis gets up from the couch and exits. Lights follow him. He speaks to the audience.)

(To the audience:) The sun was going down when I got outside. And I thought about what Nick had said to me, all that stuff about finding my place in the world, or finding some way to make a mark, and I hadn't done any of it. I hadn't made a single mark. Even at the funeral I wasn't all that important— not that many people really paid much attention to me. And it occurred to me that all I was really, was just a hole. Just an empty spot. And then I thought, I can't even believe that all I'm thinking about right now is myself. Maybe that's why I'm nothing. The whole world just goes on around me—my mom and dad are in there, hashing it out, my brother's in the ground, and I'm out here whining about the fact that I'm uncool. If I was really a good person, I'd be crying about Nick, but I'm not. I was the last person to talk to him, he even told me he was worried, in his way, and I remember during that conversation that I wanted to cut it short cause there was a good TV program coming on.

(Kimberly and Jessie enter, heading towards their house. Travis looks at them. Kimberly waves, then goes inside. Travis waves a little back as Jessie comes over.)

JESSIE: Are you doing okay, Travis?

TRAVIS: I'm fine.

JESSIE: That suit looks good on you.

TRAVIS: It's actually Nick's.

JESSIE: Oh—I'm sorry.

TRAVIS: Nah, it's all right, it doesn't fit him any more. *(Short pause.)* I mean, it didn't fit him.

    (Pause.)

JESSIE: So what are you doing tomorrow night?

TRAVIS: I don't know. Nothing.

JESSIE: We're having a sleep-over. You wanna come?

TRAVIS: To a sleep-over?

JESSIE: Well I mean it's...it's a very sophisticated sleep-over. It's more like a party really.

TRAVIS: Is your sister gonna be there?

JESSIE: Why do you care?

TRAVIS: Just wondering.

JESSIE: I don't know. She's going out to a party tonight or something.

TRAVIS: Where?

JESSIE: Why do you like her?

TRAVIS: I don't like her that much.

JESSIE: You're like totally obsessed with her. And she doesn't even know you exist.

TRAVIS: She knows I exist.

JESSIE: She knows you exist in the way she knows cockroaches exist. As long as they stay hidden in the dark and don't come around where she can see them, she's fine with it. I mean I guess that's okay because you're lurking in the bushes and all —

TRAVIS: That was one time. I lost my Frisbee —

JESSIE: Yeah you're out there throwing your Frisbee to yourself and you "accidentally" toss it into our bushes —

TRAVIS: I was not doing that on purpose —

JESSIE: Whatever. I'm just saying it's kinda sad. Most people try to play catch with at least one other person. But you got your own thing going.

TRAVIS: I was practicing —

JESSIE: Listen, let me tell you something about Kimberly. She's never going to go out with you. You know what Kimberly thinks about all day? Her hair. And her clothes. Her entire brain is filled up with that; it's like a warehouse for the mall. Okay? And you know who's she gonna go out with? Some guy just like her past nine boyfriends who has a car and money and does some kind of sport where he hurts people. That's her life. And you don't wanna be part of it, trust me.

TRAVIS: You don't know her —

JESSIE: What?! I'm her fricking sister! Have you ever talked to her?

TRAVIS: Yes —

JESSIE: About more than the weather?

TRAVIS: I talk to her all the time —

JESSIE: About homework? Leaving those sad little messages on our answering machine? What do you think she does when she hears those? First she tries to remember who you are, and then she rolls her eyes and deletes them. Okay?

TRAVIS: Well she called that one time—

JESSIE: I called. I called you.

TRAVIS: What for?

JESSIE: To make you stop leaving those stupid messages! God. You know I used to think my sister was dumb, and now I'm realizing that everyone's dumb. Maybe you two should go out. Look—she's not going to be at my party, okay? She's got other superficial-wench-type-things to be doing.

TRAVIS: How old are you again?

JESSIE: Fourteen. Practically.

TRAVIS: Aren't there any other practically fourteen year old guys you could invite instead?

JESSIE: They're all idiots. Seriously. On medication. Part monkey. Retarded.

TRAVIS: Okay, but like...I'm seventeen, okay?

JESSIE: Yeah, but you're immature for your age.

TRAVIS: Sorry.

JESSIE: You had fun last time—

TRAVIS: No I didn't—you guys tormented me the whole time.

JESSIE: Yeah but that's fun.

TRAVIS: Listen, Jessie, you are a very nice girl—and there are probably lots of guys your age—

JESSIE: *(Overlapping:)* But they're retarded!

TRAVIS: Who would love to go out with you—

JESSIE: Wait a minute, wait a minute! I'm not asking you out!

TRAVIS: Okay, fine.

JESSIE: I can ask you over to a party without asking you out.

TRAVIS: Okay, fine, you're not asking me out.

JESSIE: If I was asking you out you'd be lucky because I'm a lot hotter than any girl you're going to get—

TRAVIS: I don't know about—

JESSIE: And I'm only getting hotter. I mean, a year or two— you're going to be creeping over in the bushes trying to look into my bedroom—

TRAVIS: I lost my Frisbee in the bush!

JESSIE: Keep saying that and it might become true.

TRAVIS: It is true.

JESSIE: You know what, Travis? I might be the only person who will ever say this: but I think you're pretty cool. So come over if you want, but...if you ever need someone to actually catch that Frisbee, let me know, all right? So...

(Travis' Father exits the house.)

JESSIE: I should go.

TRAVIS: What?

JESSIE: I'm sorry about your brother. *(She gives him another quick hug:)* Bye.

TRAVIS: Bye.

TRAVIS' FATHER: What's her name again?

TRAVIS: Um... *(Realizes he doesn't know it:)* Jessie, I think.

TRAVIS' FATHER: Isn't she a little young for you to be hanging out with?

TRAVIS: Yes. Yes she is.

TRAVIS' FATHER: Oh.

(Pause.)

TRAVIS: How's Mom doing?

TRAVIS' FATHER: She's been better. *(Short pause.)* You wanna sit down?

(Travis looks around, seeing nowhere to sit except the curb.)

TRAVIS: Where?

TRAVIS' FATHER: Yeah. Yeah I guess. Uh...

TRAVIS: Are you coming home? For good?

TRAVIS' FATHER: Well that's one of the things your mother and I talked about.

TRAVIS: She misses you a lot.

TRAVIS' FATHER: I know.

TRAVIS: And I miss you. *(Pause.)* And it's really kinda mean what you've been doing.

TRAVIS' FATHER: When you're older—

TRAVIS: I understand now.

TRAVIS' FATHER: You can say that, but I don't think that you do.

TRAVIS: So are you coming home or not? *(Pause.)* You're not coming back?

TRAVIS' FATHER: To live here?

TRAVIS: Yeah that's what I'm asking!

TRAVIS' FATHER: No.

TRAVIS: Why not?

TRAVIS' FATHER: Travis, this doesn't really change things between us —

TRAVIS: What?

TRAVIS' FATHER: I mean it doesn't really alter the situation —

TRAVIS: Are you kidding me? It doesn't alter the situation?!

TRAVIS' FATHER: Between me and your mother, no.

TRAVIS: Did you see her in there?!

TRAVIS' FATHER: Yes I did and —

TRAVIS: *(Overlapping:)* She's dying in there! With you and Nick in the same month?!

TRAVIS' FATHER: *(Overlapping:)* That's unfortunate but —

TRAVIS: It's more than unfortunate! She needs you! Do you understand that? Do you know what she's been like since you've been gone? Do you care? She cries every night — you know that! There hasn't been a day I haven't come home and found her absolutely miserable wandering around the house like a ghost — she's destroyed — going through pictures, crying herself to sleep, shaking herself — and then on top of it, on top of it, just for kicks, Nick gets blown up in Iraq and you're just gonna let her drown here?!

TRAVIS' FATHER: I am not responsible for her —

TRAVIS: Yes you are!

TRAVIS' FATHER: I have to live my own life!

TRAVIS: That's the most selfish damn thing I've ever heard —

TRAVIS' FATHER: Look, I sacrificed for your mother—

TRAVIS: You did not! Oh come on—

TRAVIS' FATHER: You think this is the only time your mother has cried herself to sleep for a month! When her grandmother died, I was there—she was the same—when her Dad died, I was there, I stayed with her, I held her, I did all of that—I have been in this family—you are old enough now, you are old enough to be able to deal with this—

TRAVIS: That's what you were waiting for?

TRAVIS' FATHER: I do not love your mother. And I'm not going to stay trapped with her just because of a tragedy. You understand? I stuck it out in this marriage for a long time, and most of that had to do with you and your brother, and me being afraid to hurt her, but that's not a way to live. That's not a way to be happy. I wasn't happy—

TRAVIS: Yeah and she's happy—

TRAVIS' FATHER: She will survive. There are times in this life when you have to deal with pain, and we all have pain right now, but the response, Travis, isn't to curl up into a corner and hope that someone saves you. The response is to be strong and deal with it and live your life. And that's what I'm doing.

TRAVIS: What do you think Nick would say about that?

TRAVIS' FATHER: I think Nick would be stronger than you. I think he would understand.

TRAVIS: You're a coward. And you wreck his memory by this.

(Pause.)

TRAVIS' FATHER: Travis, I'm sorry that Nick died. I'm sorry this had to happen. I'm sorry that I had to leave. But I did not do this because of a whim, I did this because it was time, and I had to do it. And you're the one who needs to take care of your mother now, because you're all she's got. And she loved your brother very much, and I loved your brother very much, but we all deal with pain in different ways. And you need to help her. Because I can't.

TRAVIS: You won't.

TRAVIS' FATHER: I can't.

TRAVIS: You're running away from this. I don't care what you say, deep down you know you're just running away and hoping someone will clean up this mess. And by leaving you say that you don't care about me—

TRAVIS' FATHER: I care about you—

TRAVIS: You wouldn't do this if you cared. You wouldn't do this if it were me instead of him...

TRAVIS' FATHER: What do you mean by that?

TRAVIS: You know what I mean.

TRAVIS' FATHER: You want me to say I loved him more?

TRAVIS: It's true, isn't it?

TRAVIS' FATHER: No. It's not. I love you both.

TRAVIS: Say that all you want, but we both know it's true. I know what you think of me. You got one son who's a hero and one who's just there. I know the difference between me and him. Why are you leaving now, that he's gone? You're leaving cause you don't want anything to do with us, like you're caught in a beartrap and you're sawing off you own leg to escape.

TRAVIS' FATHER: I love you and your brother the same —

TRAVIS: You can't even say that convincingly.

TRAVIS' FATHER: Travis —

TRAVIS: Go on, get out of here. If you're leaving, if you need to escape so badly that you can't even stick around to help out after your favorite son's funeral, go ahead. I feel sorry for you. Because you gotta live the rest of your life being you. And I'm happy because I get to live the rest of my life being me. And one of these days, when you're in your crappy little California apartment, and you're lonely, and you got no life, and you got a crappy job, and you think about running on back here to see if we still need you: We won't. We won't need you. And you're going to be stuck out there lonely and sad and miserable because you had love in your life and you trashed it. So get out.

(Pause.)

TRAVIS' FATHER: I didn't kill Nick. And I'm sorry that you think I loved him more than you — and you know what, if we're being honest here, maybe I did. And I don't know if that's something I can help or what.

TRAVIS: You know what Dad? It doesn't matter that you had more love for him, all that matters is that you have so little of it for me.

TRAVIS' FATHER: I'm sorry.

(He starts to leave.)

TRAVIS: No you're not.

(Travis' Father looks back for a moment, then exits. Travis stands there. Lights shift. Loud, angry music far away. Erynne enters.)

ERYNNE: The thing is: I don't really hate myself. You know, I mean that's what people think. They see someone like me, and they see me now, and they think, that girl hates herself. She's got self-esteem issues. I don't hate myself. I'm afraid. I'm afraid of the future. I'm afraid of my future. And that's something that keeps me up at night, and I wake up, terrified, not of the darkness, but of the growing unease with the world around me. And so somehow, all of this, all of this piling on top of me, I feel like I'm underwater, and the whole world is burning around me. And I want to join in with the flames.

(The music gets louder.)

So I went to this party. Cause what else are you gonna do?

(Erynne drifts to the side as the party forms around her. Trank is visible first, carrying in a tank of something. Others emerge from different areas of the stage. Nemo, Chubb, Scooter, Esmerelda, and others. Kimberly stands near the back, talking with her friend, KATIE. Both seem somewhat disgusted and thrilled by the situation. Erynne is on the periphery, unnoticed by the others.)

TRANK: Check this out!

CHUBB: Praise Jesus!

TRANK: Hey, hey, shut up with that. I'm serious.

CHUBB: Whatever.

TRANK: Who's house is this anyway?

NEMO: My cousin's.

CHUBB: Where are they?

NEMO: They're gone for the weekend.

TRANK: Sweet.

(He picks up something and throws it.)

NEMO: Come on, show a little respect.

TRANK: Sorry. *(He throws something more respectfully:)* What? Had to be done, man.

(They set about getting things ready. Kimberly speaks with her friend.)

KIMBERLY: You didn't tell me this was gonna be druggie party.

KATIE: It's not.

KIMBERLY: Look at these people. They're freaks.

(Trank is eating something disgusting.)

KATIE: Do you know that guy, Nemo?

KIMBERLY: I've seen him before.

KATIE: Just chill out all right, it'll be fine.

(Scooter approaches them. He stands there looking at them, not saying anything. They try to avoid him by moving away. He follows.)

KIMBERLY: Excuse me? Do I know you?

SCOOTER: Do you want to know me?

KATIE: Hey I know you! Your name's Brian, right!

SCOOTER: Scooter.

KATIE: No, your name's Brian! We went to Elementary School together! Oh—Dude, look at you, you're totally messed up now! You must've been doing tons of drugs!

SCOOTER: I was once known as Brian.

KATIE: Yeah—we had homeroom together. Remember me? Katie?

(He looks at her strangely.)

SCOOTER: Yes.

KATIE: Oh wow. So what's going on?

SCOOTER: I need your help. *(He closes in on them:)* I just received a disturbing phone call. *(He pauses for effect:)* Have any of you ever heard of the Evil Time Computer?

(Pause.)

KIMBERLY: No.

SCOOTER: It is a device created in the future, which has achieved sentience—

KIMBERLY: What?

SCOOTER: Sentience.

KIMBERLY: Oh. That.

SCOOTER: And with its sentience it has determined that human beings are to be exterminated.

KIMBERLY: Isn't that the plot of Terminator?

KATIE: So wait—the evil time computer called you on the phone?

SCOOTER: Yes. To mock me.

KIMBERLY: Hey Katie maybe we should go over there.

KATIE: You know that's not a bad idea—

(They try to leave, but Scooter stops them.)

SCOOTER: Just so you know. I may need to love you tonight.

(Pause. Kimberly and Katie move in separate directions.)

KIMBERLY: Okay. That's nice. Bye.

(They escape. More people enter.)

TRANK: Hey! Come on in!

(Esmerelda approaches Scooter.)

ESMERELDA: What did I tell you about talking to strangers?

SCOOTER: A stranger is just a friend you haven't met.

ESMERELDA: A stranger is someone who's going to put you in a mental home.

SCOOTER: That's where they want me.

(Nemo finds Kimberly.)

NEMO: What's up?

KIMBERLY: Not much.

NEMO: Your name is...

KIMBERLY: Kimberly.

NEMO: Right. You're a prep, right? No, that's cool. No judgments. It takes all kinds.

KIMBERLY: Right. What's your name? Nemo? Like the fish?

NEMO: Yup. I was the original though. Actually I'm Captain Nemo.

KIMBERLY: Oh you're a captain?

NEMO: Yeah. So look, are you here to have a good time or what?

KIMBERLY: What do you mean by that?

NEMO: Whatever.

KIMBERLY: Not with you.

NEMO: Look at that, I'm not even saying anything, and you've got this attitude all of a sudden. No that's cool, you just go around and enjoy my house and drink my drinks and make yourself at home, all right? Try not to be an ungrateful skank, though. It hurts your image. I mean you got this thing going on, right?

(Opposite, Erynne enters.)

KIMBERLY: What thing?

NEMO: This um...`I'm better than you' thing. How's that work for you? You make a lot of friends that way? Cause let me tell you what I see when I look at you, okay? Let's see, you spend a lot of time on your hair, cause you think that makes you special. And you really like feeling special all the time cause deep down you're afraid you're not all that smart or interesting or anything, so you better make sure your hair is perfect cause otherwise no one's gonna look at you. And you like to be looked at, don't you? Reminds you that you exist, cause otherwise you just might fade out of existence.

KIMBERLY: Piss off. <Go away.>

NEMO: Hey that's cool.

(He spots Erynne and goes over to her.)

What's up?

ERYNNE: What were you doing talking to that girl?

NEMO: What girl?

ERYNNE: That chick from my history class.

NEMO: What's your problem?

ERYNNE: Just what were you doing over there?

NEMO: I can't talk to other girls?

ERYNNE: Well, yeah, but—

NEMO: Whatever.

(Chubb comes over.)

CHUBB: Hey guys.

ERYNNE: What's going on?

(Nemo gives Chubb a look.)

CHUBB: Oh. Right. I'll see you later.

ERYNNE: What was that about?

NEMO: Hey can we talk?

ERYNNE: We're talking now.

NEMO: I mean, you know, away from everyone.

ERYNNE: Um...okay.

(Nemo takes Erynne outside.)

What's up? *(Pause.)* What's going on? Talk to me, what's wrong?

NEMO: So uh...I've been thinking about this a lot. And...I'll just come out and say this—I think we should break up. *(Pause.)* Because...I don't think you're happy—

ERYNNE: The reason I'm not happy isn't you!

NEMO: Right. But...

ERYNNE: Why do you wanna break up with me?

NEMO: I'm trying to tell you. Okay—I don't think we're happy together...and it seems like all I do is make you miserable and I'm just not...I don't wanna be your therapist any more. Okay?

ERYNNE: Well maybe I could do something and—

NEMO: I don't think so.

ERYNNE: There's gotta be something I can do. I'm sorry, maybe I just talk too much, maybe I won't lay all of that on you any more and we can stay together—

NEMO: We've tried that—

ERYNNE: But I'll really do it this time. And you know, if you need space, I can give you that, and, you know, anything you want, okay?

NEMO: No.

ERYNNE: Ah come on!

NEMO: Erynne—

ERYNNE: You can't just do this! You can't just decide this!

NEMO: Yes I can.

ERYNNE: It's not fair! You didn't even give me a chance to talk about it with you—how long have you been thinking about this?!

NEMO: A couple of days.

ERYNNE: A couple of days that's it?! That's all it takes for you to throw us in the garbage—I'm sorry, throw me in the garbage, and you're in there hitting on another chick already and you haven't even dumped me yet?

NEMO: All right—chill out.

ERYNNE: I hope you rot! I hope you get some kinda horrible disease from that skank—

(*Erynne tries to move back toward the party.*)

NEMO: Where are you going?

ERYNNE: I'm gonna go take that bitch <chick> out—

NEMO: She has nothing to do with it!

ERYNNE: Let go of me!

NEMO: Erynne. Chill out. This is not her fault. All right? I've been thinking about this for a while. I don't want to go out with you any more. You're depressed all the time.

ERYNNE: Yeah this'll help with that. Thanks. Thanks for cheering me up.

NEMO: And I don't wanna deal with that any more—

ERYNNE: Well that's nice for you. That you can just shrug me off like a...raincoat or something. I'm sorry I'm depressed, all right? I'm sorry I got kicked out of my house and was living in a car. I'm sorry I can't find a place to sleep. I didn't realize what a burden that was on you. I was too busy trying to stay alive, okay? And I'm really sorry that I tried to lean on you when my whole life was falling apart, and is falling apart, and has fallen completely apart, I'm sorry that I wasn't emotionally strong enough to be able to handle that and just have sex all the time instead of worrying about what I'm going to eat. I realize now that I was a terrible girlfriend and I apologize for not being some brainless bimbo with her own car and a college savings and a rainbow-colored pony burned onto my brain. Sorry. I have other things to think about. So maybe I'll just run off and kill myself so you won't have to deal with "that" any more. Okay? That sound good?

NEMO: Look—

ERYNNE: Don't touch me!

(She storms past him back into the house. Chubb comes over.)

CHUBB: I'm so sorry, Erynne.

ERYNNE: You knew about this?

CHUBB: He told me earlier.

(Erynne kicks at something and pushes past her.)

Hey come on—

(Erynne slams a door. Lights shift slightly. Nemo is still outside. Travis enters, talking to the audience.)

TRAVIS: So I just started walking. And I guess somewhere in my mind I figured I wanted to find Kimberly, and maybe that would be enough. And then I thought—I need one good thing. That's what I need today: One Good Thing. Cause there's too much, you know? And when it seems like one thing goes bad, then all of a sudden everything is, and you don't even know how to deal with it. And all I need, really, is one moment, you know, where something goes my way. And then I'll make it.

NEMO: What's going on?

TRAVIS: Nothing.

NEMO: You coming to the party?

TRAVIS: Yeah I guess.

NEMO: Two bucks.

TRAVIS: What?

NEMO: Two bucks admission.

TRAVIS: Oh. Um...

(Travis begins searching for his wallet.)

Shoot. I don't have my wallet on me.

NEMO: You don't have two bucks?

TRAVIS: Can you let it slide?

(Pause.)

NEMO: Sorry, man. If I did it for you, I'd have to do it for everybody.

TRAVIS: Maybe I'll just, you know, not drink anything.

NEMO: Dude, I mean, you know if you were a cool guy or something, I'd let you in, but...man, I'm just messing with you, there's no cover.

TRAVIS: Oh!

NEMO: No there is. Two bucks.

TRAVIS: Wait I—

NEMO: Nah, I'm messing with you again. Go on in.

(Travis enters the party. He looks around at the people, doesn't see Kimberly initially. Then he spots her, illuminated in a shaft of light.)

TRAVIS: There she was.

(Travis is about to walk towards her when Scooter scoots past him and approaches first. She tries to ignore him.)

SCOOTER: When I tell you to, duck!

KIMBERLY: What?

SCOOTER: And then run to my van. You'll be safe there.

KIMBERLY: Um... Hey look, it's my boyfriend! *(She waves at Travis:)* Hey Travis, honey. Look...Brian—

SCOOTER: Scooter.

KIMBERLY: Scooter, it's my boyfriend, Travis. Travis, Scooter. Scooter, Travis.

TRAVIS: Hi.

SCOOTER: You are in danger.

KIMBERLY: We're all in danger.

TRAVIS: Why is that?

KIMBERLY: Because the Evil Time Computer is coming back in time to erase us all.

(She makes a crazy sign with her fingers and points to Scooter.)

TRAVIS: Oh yeah. I heard about that.

KIMBERLY: You know what we should do, Travis? We should run for it.

TRAVIS: Sounds good.

(He looks around for a moment, grabs Kimberly's hand, and dashes toward the door with her. Scooter looks around confused for a moment.)

SCOOTER: They're weird.

(Travis and Kimberly make it outside, laughing.)

KIMBERLY: Oh my God, that guy has been following me around all night.

TRAVIS: Who is he?

KIMBERLY: I don't know, he's some totally freaky guy. He said he needed to love me in his van.

TRAVIS: Ewww...

KIMBERLY: I know. *(She shakes:)* I lost my friend Katie so I've been trying to escape that guy for the past hour. He says I contain all the secrets of the universe. *(She shakes again:)* Thank you for saving me.

TRAVIS: Hey what are neighbors for?

KIMBERLY: Right. *(She looks at him:)* You didn't change from the funeral?

TRAVIS: I thought I looked good in the suit.

KIMBERLY: All right, well I'll see you later.

(She starts to leave.)

TRAVIS: Where are you going?

KIMBERLY: I'm outta here.

TRAVIS: Oh. So what are you doing now?

KIMBERLY: Going home.

TRAVIS: Oh. It's only midnight.

KIMBERLY: Yeah, but this is a party for freaks. I just came cause Katie wanted me to.

TRAVIS: Right.

KIMBERLY: All right, well, bye.

TRAVIS: Wait a minute.

KIMBERLY: What?

TRAVIS: Um... You wanna do something?

KIMBERLY: With you?

TRAVIS: Yeah, you know, we could go to like...Denny's or something.

KIMBERLY: I hate Denny's.

TRAVIS: Me too. But a similar restaurant. Also open 24 hours.

KIMBERLY: Why?

TRAVIS: To hang out.

KIMBERLY: Um...

TRAVIS: Or we could like watch a movie or something.

KIMBERLY: Travis. No. I think you'd get the wrong idea.
All right?

TRAVIS: Yeah, sure.

KIMBERLY: Good night.

TRAVIS: See ya around.

(She leaves. Travis is left outside. Lights shift. Erynne is alone in the bathroom. Music begins. She's shivering and cold, slumped to her side. A bottle of pills, unopened, rests in her hand.)

ERYNNE: I guess the thing is no one wants you. I mean, I don't know. They all got other things to do, you know? Cause you're not...I mean...you're not—you're not good enough, you're not worth it, you're not really anything anyone wants around. Ever. *(She curls up, looking at the bottle:)* And you're just fooling yourself if you think anyone cares...or would care...and all of a sudden you'll end up being really popular when you're dead—'oh I was friends with her' 'we were really good friends' 'it hurts so much' and they'll all stand around crying and wondering why...but they still won't care. That's just what you do to fake it. Make you feel better, make you think you were next to a tragedy, you know? It makes you so special. *(She looks at them again:)* But I guess it really comes down to do I want to be here tomorrow? Have it hurt when I get up, have it hurt all day long, all hollowed out, trailing blood wherever I go. I don't want to be that. I don't want to be here any more. So...

(She considers the pills once again, twitching in nervousness. Suddenly she grabs a handful of them and begins the arduous process of swallowing pills. She begins in a nervous fit, but slows down and begins doing it consciously, taking handfuls of pills and swallowing them in measured gulps. She gets up,

glassy eyed, then bends over in pain. DIERDRE enters, dressed for the party.)

DIERDRE: Hey sis. What's up?

(No response.)

Rough day, huh? Kind of a clichéd way to go, don't you think? A girl takes a whole bunch of pills? Man that's nothing. That won't even make the news. I mean, you know, as long as you're planning on checking out, you might as well, you know, really get into it. You just got yourself locked into the bathroom here. They won't even notice.

(Erynne crouches in a kind of sleepy pain.)

What's the matter?

(Erynne tries to say something.)

What was that? Look, I'm just a hallucination brought on by a massive dose of... *(She checks the bottle:)* Sominex. Well you got the right bottle at least. At least it wasn't Ex-Lax or something. Here. *(She opens the door:)* The party's waiting.

(Erynne emerges into the party. Everyone is there, except for Travis. The MUSIC grows louder and stranger now. Everything appears to be slowing down. Snatches of conversation are heard, but nothing is clear, nothing makes sense.)

ESMERELDA: —Why can't you just be normal?

TRANK: Well that's when I found Jesus—

PERSON #1: Dude, that chick is totally wasted—

CHUBB: You have no idea—

SCOOTER: My brother knows many things—

PERSON #2: I was like, get outta my face—

TRANK: That's when I found Jesus —

CHUBB: You have no idea —

PERSON #1: That chick's totally wasted —

CHUBB: Are you all right?

ESMERELDA: Why don't you just go home —

PERSON #3: I never even liked that guy —

SCOOTER: It is coming for us —

> *(The sound from the music and the voices is suddenly extinguished. Erynne topples to the floor. Everyone stares at her. Pause. Dierdre leans in over her. Everyone else is frozen.)*

DIERDRE: Wait here a second. The world is grinding to a halt. All the stars are crumbling from the sky. You could die right here in front of everyone. Is that what you want?

> *(Pause. The MUSIC roars up again as Erynne staggers to her feet, barely conscious. Voices again.)*

Suit yourself.

PERSON #2: Dude, check that out.

PERSON #1: That chick thinks she's better than everyone.

CHUBB: Are you all right?

PERSON #3: She's totally freaking out —

PERSON #1: What's her name?

PERSON #4: God I hate that chick.

PERSON #2: Why does she look like that?

PERSON #3: What do you think she's trying to prove —

PERSON #1: On drugs —

PERSON #2: Messed up —

PERSON #3: Freaked out —

PERSON #4: Skank.

PERSON #1: I'd hate to be her.

(Erynne staggers outside. The music becomes quieter.)

DIERDRE: Feel the air. Last time. Feel the ground. Last time. Look around you. Bye now. See you soon.

(Erynne stumbles forward, falling to the ground. She lands directly at Travis' feet. All music and sound stop. Dierdre disappears. Pause. Travis looks at her.)

TRAVIS: Are you all right?

(He touches her, looks around. There is no one nearby.)

Are you okay? Does anyone know this girl!

(No answer. He makes a vain attempt to check her pulse, but doesn't quite know what to do. He makes a move back toward the house, then stops, pulling out his cell phone. He dials 911.)

Yeah, hello? This is an emergency — *(He looks around for an address:)* 1624 Randolph Avenue. Yeah there's a girl here who's passed out. She's like, she doesn't look like she's breathing — I don't know. I don't know her. Uh huh. Yeah, I'll stay right here. Do you want me to stay on the line? Okay, okay. *(He hangs up and looks down at her body:)* Hey. Come on. Come on wake up. It's not that bad. *(He stops, then tries to roll her over on her side:)* I know you. I know you. You're in my class. You're gonna be okay. We're all gonna be okay. *(Short pause.)* Did you do the reading for Monday? I totally forgot what we were supposed to do. *(He tries to laugh a little bit, then focuses on her again:)* What's your name? My name's Travis. We're gonna make it. Okay? We're gonna make it.

(The lights fade on them. Lights flashing. Sirens. Lights up on the waiting area of the hospital. Clean, antiseptic lighting. Travis sits nervously in a chair. A NURSE emerges, holding a clipboard.)

NURSE: Travis Arneson?

TRAVIS: Yeah.

NURSE: If you could please fill this out.

TRAVIS: Sure. Is she gonna be...

NURSE: They're pumping her stomach now.

TRAVIS: I mean is she uh...

NURSE: It's too soon to tell. Are you related to her?

TRAVIS: Yeah. She's uh...my sister.

NURSE: Do you have a number where your parents can be reached?

TRAVIS: They're out of town.

NURSE: Okay. Well we'll let you know when something happens.

TRAVIS: Thanks.

(Lights shift as the Nurse exits. Travis addresses the audience.)

(To the audience:) So I sat there. And I waited. With this girl who I should've known but I didn't. With this girl who I wouldn't have cared about on any other day. And I just thought that things were bad enough without this thing happening too. So I prayed and I asked my brother that maybe if he saw this girl, he could send her back. So after about an hour...

(The Nurse returns.)

NURSE: You can go in now.

(Lights shift to the hospital room. Erynne, looking pale and exhausted, is lying in the bed, awake. Travis enters gingerly.)

TRAVIS: Hi.

(She looks at him.)

ERYNNE: Travis? Is that your name?

TRAVIS: Yeah. You know it. And um...what's yours?

ERYNNE: Erynne.

TRAVIS: Hi.

ERYNNE: Hi.

TRAVIS: So... How're you feeling?

ERYNNE: Like Hell.

TRAVIS: You're alive.

(She nods.)

The doctors said it was touch and go.

ERYNNE: I'm lucky.

TRAVIS: Yeah.

(Pause.)

ERYNNE: Thank you for saving my life.

TRAVIS: I didn't have anything else to do.

(She tries to laugh a little bit.)

I guess I should let you rest.

ERYNNE: You mind staying here with me...a little while?

TRAVIS: I don't mind.

ERYNNE: Thanks.

(Travis speaks to the audience.)

TRAVIS: So I stayed there for four hours, and when she woke up again, she said she wanted to go for a walk. Cause she liked walks. And I thought that was a pretty stupid idea, cause it was something like five in the morning and here she was on the edge of death and all, but we decided to go anyway, and we had to sneak out past the nurses cause we weren't supposed to go anywhere. But we escaped from the hospital, and on the way she told me all about her and I told her all about me, and how it was funny that we had never actually met this whole time. And anyway, just about five thirty, we ended up in the parking lot of one of my favorite places:

ERYNNE: Big Lots. This place sucks.

TRAVIS: No it's pretty cool. Check it out, there's actually a ladder in the back they leave out sometimes, and you can sneak up to the roof and see the whole town.

ERYNNE: I don't wanna see the whole town.

TRAVIS: No it's actually pretty beautiful, come on.

(They find the ladder and start scaling it.)

Come on, I'll help you.

ERYNNE: I don't know if I can climb this thing.

TRAVIS: It's not that hard, come on.

(Erynne climbs the ladder shakily. Travis leads Erynne on to the roof of the Big Lots. They sit. The sun begins to rise. Quiet.)

ERYNNE: You ever wonder what happens when we die?

TRAVIS: You almost found out.

ERYNNE: I know.

TRAVIS: Did you—I mean was there like a flash of light or anything? Like, you know, a "step into the light" kind of thing?

ERYNNE: Felt more like being buried in sand.

TRAVIS: Huh.

ERYNNE: But you know, I was drugged-up.

TRAVIS: Maybe you only get the flash of light if you pick a better way to go.

ERYNNE: Yeah, I guess.

TRAVIS: So what are you gonna do now?

ERYNNE: I don't know.

TRAVIS: We got a spare bedroom at my house.

ERYNNE: Nick's?

TRAVIS: No no—another bedroom besides that one.

ERYNNE: Oh.

TRAVIS: It's pretty lonely there now. Maybe you could stay there.

ERYNNE: Maybe. You know I haven't even told my parents yet?

TRAVIS: You probably should.

ERYNNE: Why? Why should they know? I think maybe I'll get myself cleaned up and then go back there in a few months and be like, "I survived." Cause I did survive, you know? I feel like I've been given a second chance, and I'm not gonna waste it. I'm through it now. On the other side. So when I go back there, and I'm graduating, and I'm cleaned up, and I got a good life and a job and everything, I wonder what they're gonna think? Cause I'm not the same as my sister, as much as they think I am.

TRAVIS: That's good.

ERYNNE: And you're not your brother either.

TRAVIS: I know that. You know, while I was at his funeral; I mean, I didn't cry, and I really wanted to cry, I wanted to feel it, you know? But all I could think about was how many people were there, there were like two hundred people there, and I figured that if it was my funeral there'd be like twenty, you know? And that it was funny, even in death, my brother was more popular than me. And I thought, what kind of sick bastard thinks about this at his only brother's funeral? What's wrong with me? I shoulda been thinking about all the fun we used to have, and all the times he was there for me, even though he was kind of a jerk about it, and all those good things about his life that were ending now. And what he taught me, and how he helped me, and how even though he was a pain in the butt he was a good brother, and even though he didn't show it very often, he loved me. I mean, that's the thing, he loved me. I don't know that I loved him back. *(Pause.)* He was right, though, I need to make something out of myself. Something more than I've been.

ERYNNE: Yeah. Hey look, the sun's coming up.

TRAVIS: Yeah.

ERYNNE: You're right. The town does look beautiful from here.

TRAVIS: It's really all about perspective.

ERYNNE: You know why it's beautiful?

TRAVIS: Why?

ERYNNE: Because I can't see the Big Lots.

TRAVIS: Shut up. *(Pause.)* Hey Erynne?

ERYNNE: Yeah?

TRAVIS: What are you doing in April?

ERYNNE: I don't know. Staying alive.

TRAVIS: You want to go to the Prom with me?

ERYNNE: Sure.

(Travis smiles, reaches out, and holds her hand. Lights fade out.)

(End of play.)

The Author Speaks

What inspired you to write this play?
I wanted to write a play that accurately reflected the lives of my students. There's a strange thing going on in the world of high school theatre: we tend to do classics, and then wonder why students feel that theatre doesn't *speak* to them. In the early twentieth century, new modern plays were produced on Broadway that had huge casts. They were easily adopted to the high school stage and were performed everywhere. *The Crucible* and *You Can't Take it With You* are perfect examples of this. As the economics of Broadway changed, however, plays with large casts became cost-prohibitive. It was simply too expensive to hire all those actors. So the plays, and the subjects they dealt with, began to shrink. Today, most new plays on Broadway (when there are any) are tiny (and often their subject matter is not something that would be deemed permissible on high school stages), so they don't get done in high schools. All this is to say that we face a crisis in high school theatre. Students don't feel that theatre is a modern, engaging, living art form. With *One Good Thing* I wanted to write a large-cast play that was about them, the lives they were living. I wanted it to deal with the difficulties my kids were facing, and I wanted it to be raw and real. I was also heavily influenced by the music of Meatloaf. It's ridiculous, I know, it's a really, really stupid thing to say. But I loved the operatic nature of his songs, how they dealt with teenage angst and heartbreak and joy—I wanted this play to be like one of his songs.

Was the structure of the play influenced by any other work?
Not that I think of off-hand. The structure of the play is interesting, in that it has two protagonists who run in parallel lines and don't meet until the very end. I always liked the

structure of this one.

Have you dealt with the same theme in other works that you have written?
Yes, although most of my other work tends to be more comedic in nature. I've dealt with some heavy material in a few of my full-length plays, but never to this extent. If anything, this is a throwback to the type of plays I was writing in college—more character-driven, more personality-based. Except now that I have a lot of experience writing for the stage, I'm more confident that I can keep a story progressing forward.

What writers have had the most profound effect on your style?
Interesting question. It's so hard to say. I've seen and read a lot of plays, and I'm sure all of them have influenced me in ways both subtle and direct. I love the aggressive nature of Albee, and the emotional truth of Tennessee Williams and O'Neill—I love the unspoken desperation of Chekhov and the playfulness of Kushner. There are just so many writers I love and admire; I'm not sure I could point to one and say that they are the major influence on me.

What do you hope to achieve with this work?
I want kids to feel that theatre is alive and that it speaks to them. I want them to see people on stage who resemble them, who are going through similar circumstances—above all, a play is an exercise in empathy. The actors must empathize with the characters they are playing, and the audience gets a chance to connect with people who they might not normally connect with. We're allowed and encouraged to see other lives as equal to our own in the theatre, and that's a massive thing for a teenager to understand.

What are the most common mistakes that occur in productions of your work?
I think people get too jokey with a lot of them. Yes there are jokes, and yes the plays should make the audience laugh. But there are times when mugging for a laugh destroys the coherence and reality of the world you're portraying. You have to play these things as dead-serious as possible — don't *believe* that you're funny — just chase down your objective.

What inspired you to become a playwright?
I've wanted to be a writer for as long as I can remember. I didn't get into theater until I was a junior in high school, but once I got on stage I was hooked. I didn't connect my two passions, acting and writing, until college though. We had a weekly group that met in a tiny theatre under my dorm — each Friday night writers would hand out scripts to actors and they would be read out loud. It wasn't anything as formal as a workshop, it was just a lot of fun — mostly a lot of people clowning around. I wrote my first piece around January of my freshman year, and I got such a positive result from the audience I kept going. It was great to have people applaud and laugh and occasionally cry because of something I'd written. You can't get that energy while writing a novel.

How did you research the subject?
Listening to my students. They were all going through similar things to the characters in the play. Some of them had siblings in the military, some of them had absent fathers, or were having huge difficulties at home. I just listened, and then invented the rest.

Shakespeare gave advice to the players in *Hamlet*; if you could give advice to your cast what would it be?

The same advice that Shakespeare gave: be truthful. Don't try to play the emotions of the scene, try to connect with the desires of the characters and let the emotions come through that. And project. And cheat out. And don't upstage yourself. And hold for laughs.

How was the first production different from the vision that you created in your mind?
I directed the first production, so I had a lot to do with both. Honestly, I try not to picture things too specifically when I write. That way, I'm never too disappointed with the production. I try to come into both facets of the work fresh.

About the Author

Don Zolidis is a former high school and middle school theatre teacher and is currently a professor of creative writing at Ursinus College. Originally hailing from Wisconsin, Mr. Zolidis received his B.A. in English from Carleton College and an MFA in Playwriting from the Actor's Studio Program at the New School. He has received numerous honors, including the 2004 Princess Grace Award for Playwriting for *White Buffalo*, now published by Samuel French. His plays have appeared or been workshopped professionally at the Ensemble Studio Theatre, Stage West, Purple Rose Theatre, The Victory Theatre, Bloomington Playwright's Project, Chattyboo Productions, Mirror Stage Company, Impetuous Theatre Group, and New Dramatists. His plays have had amateur productions in all 50 states and 16 countries and have won numerous state championships. His screenplays have received numerous prizes, including the 2009 PAGE gold medal for drama, 1st prize in the family division for both the 2008 Screenwriting Expo and 2008 StoryPros Contest and several others. He has one screenplay under option with Will

Ferrell's Gary Sanchez Productions and a second in development with an independent producer. He lives with his wife and his two adorable boys.

More from YouthPLAYS

Harry's Hotter at Twilight by Jonathan Dorf

Comedy. 90-100 minutes. 5-25+ males, 7-25+ females (12-50+ performers possible).

In this crazed mash-up parody of *Harry Potter* and *Twilight*— with cameos crashing in from *Lord of the Rings*, *Star Wars*, *Alice in Wonderland* and many other places—you'll encounter deli-owning vegetarians, invisible rabbits, magical carrot weapons, random lunatics, soothing offstage voices, evil gourmets and much more, as everyone's favorite wizards, vampires and werewolves battle to save miserable, gloomy Spork—and indeed the world—from certain destruction.

Lockdown by Julia Edwards

Dramedy. 75-90 minutes. 4-6 males, 9-11 females (15 performers possible).

It's just another day in the CliffsNotes Library (more books, less filling!) until a siren sounds, the doors automatically lock, and the not-so-studious students discover they are trapped. What's going on? Did the high-tech security system malfunction again? Or are they the subjects of a sinister state-sanctioned experiment? Then someone hears a gunshot (he thinks), a freaked out substitute teacher is found barricaded in the bathroom, and Crazy Lily has a diabetic seizure. In a claustrophobic pressure-cooker of fear, paranoia, and social strife, this motley crew of hackers, delinquents, surfer dudes, and prom queens must rise above the chaos to save a life and discover the meaning of tolerance along the way.

Printed in Great Britain
by Amazon

64826891R00068